The Environmental Audit and Business Strategy

A Total Quality Approach

The Environmental Audit and Business Strategy

A Total Quality Approach

GRANT LEDGERWOOD
ELIZABETH STREET
RIKI THERIVEL

FINANCIAL TIMES

PITMAN PUBLISHING

Pitman Publishing
128 Long Acre, London WC2E 9AN

A Division of Longman Group UK Limited

First published in 1992

© Grant Ledgerwood, Elizabeth Street, Riki Therivel, 1992

British Library Cataloguing in Publication Data
A CIP catalogue record for this book can be
obtained from the British Library

ISBN 0 273 03850 8

Phototypset in Linotron Times Roman
by Northern Phototypesetting Co. Ltd., Bolton
Printed and bound in Great Britain by Biddles Ltd., Guildford

CONTENTS

'The marketplace is saying there is a change on, a new kind of social thinking. I believe at the moment that there is a base being built for something big to happen in the '90s. It is a revival of social activism, coupled with an increasing level of concern for the environment. It is not the angry protestor of the '60s who has a vision of the future and passion for the moment. The new word in the marketplace is values – and what consumers want are companies making socially responsible products or providing socially responsible services.'

Anita Roddick, OBE, director-founder of Body Shop International plc, the most successful consumer goods company of the 1990s; from her MacMillan Education Lecture at the conference of the Geographical Association 19 April 1990. Published in *Geography* 1991

Dedicated to Tim; and to Kate and Matt and all the new generation who will be achieving global sustainability.

PREFACE

Bringing environmental issues into the core of business strategy is the central focus of this book. Under present regulatory developments in the OECD countries, corporate environmental strategies are becoming integral to legal and financial systems of business. Yet, if this change is to be successful, there can be nothing mechanistic about its planning and implementation. There must be the greatest concern with marketing, persuasion, leadership, motivation and personal communications, which is essential both inside and outside the company. Only by so doing can the environmental manager succeed in ensuring that the business both complies with the new codes and also is on the way to becoming a benign partner with our physical environment. The text is intended to approach these issues with a methodical scheme of analysis and set of procedures for implementing corporate environmental programmes.

The focus of the book is on integrating environmental audit into standard business settings, both at the strategic and the programme-operational levels. The issues of business and the environment are summarised in Part I. Parts II and III, the heart of this text, focus on how the manager can build a career in the corporate setting with an environmental programme. Thus, implementability is a clear emphasis and occupies Parts II and III. The book aims to be practical as well as provocative. It focuses on methods: what is the nature of the procedure by which a valid and credible environmental strategy can be developed for the business?

The text is targeted particularly at managers and students who have trained on business administration and management courses. It aims to provide the components of an educational sequence for managers taking on, or planning to take on, an environmental management responsibility for their company. The younger manager may have direct operational responsibility for a recycling or waste management operation. The middle manager or corporate planner might be assuming new supervisory responsibilities or planning agendas involving environmental issues. The strategic manager and senior executive may need to plan key problems of legal compliance, investment strategy, liability, insurance and investor communications from an environmental perspective.

The businesses involved will include voluntary and governmental enterprises, which make up 35 to 50 per cent of the economies of advanced industrial states. Their environmental responsibilities reach even deeper than those of the business corporation itself, for they have social and charitable goals, all of which have environmental sustainability dimensions.

The text is also aimed at investment analysts and investors, whose companies need to find the right balance between environmental and financial targets. Many ethical investment strategists, for instance, are seeking to understand how companies are implementing the green revolution in their business strategy. They are assisted by a raft of specialist newsletters and bulletins on green investment, and in the UK by a recent and comprehensive book by Adams *et al.*, *Changing Corporate Values* (1991), which sets up an evaluation matrix for many large companies' corporate environmental impacts. This book provides such investors with guidance on how to decide which companies will achieve competitive advantage and consequent investment attractiveness.

On a personal note, the environmental agenda appears finally to be advancing rapidly. Recent developments include the adoption of the US environmental audit procedure of 1986 and the environmental aspects of the Single European Act of 1987. But the environmental crisis goes some way back, to Rachel Carson's seminal book *Silent Spring* (1962). The maturing of the marginal academic concerns of the 1960s into the hard legal and financial realities of the 1990s, a lag of 30 years, is indicative of the time period for major new issues to influence the cornerstone elements of complex economies. Let us hope that we are in time to avert a collision between our successful economic engines and the natural environment so critical to their sustenance.

ACKNOWLEDGEMENTS

A book in the field of Environmental Audit and corporate strategy synthesises from multiple sources and therefore draws on existing books, technical handbooks and articles. We have relied on our contacts in industry and academia for the preliminary review of specific chapters and of the text as a whole.

Because of the range of issues it tackles, a book such as this synthesises across the work of consultants, academics and researchers spanning recent decades. In particular, the book should be seen as complementary to John Elkington and colleagues' *The Green Business Guide* (1991).

Our approach is at the corporate policy and programme level. For application of specific audit operations and projects, we recommend Lawrence Cahill's authoritative *Environmental Audits* (6th edn.), the American government handbook on the field published by the Government Press Institute Inc. Many of its detailed procedures and protocols are essential in developing best practice internationally and it is hoped that an international edition will be published. In the mean time, it is indispensable for the operating practitioner of environmental audit, in spite of its US orientation.

Our publisher colleagues at Pitman *Financial Times*, namely Helen Pilgrim, Henry Reece and Julie Hughes, and their colleagues in Covent Garden, London, have shown enthusiasm and efficiency.

Among colleagues who have assisted and advised on various stages of this book are Philip Nicholson, a leading environmental assessment consultant in Ottawa; Dr Malcolm Hutton, environmental audit consultant and ecotoxicologist, London; and the following, who are all from the University of Greenwich, Dr Ivan Vince, Visiting Research Fellow, School of Environmental Science; Anthony Levy of the Business Strategy Division; and Dr Carla Millar, Director of the International Management Research and Innovation Centre.

In spite of their and our efforts, there remain omissions and mistakes in this initial overview of a complex and rapidly developing field. We take responsibility for these errors and gaps and ask for readers' communications to draw our attention to improvements for future editions.

We acknowledge and are grateful for permission to use texts, figures and direct quotations from the following sources:

Figure 2.1 is taken from Elkington *et al. The Green Business Guide*, 'Industries in the Firing Line', by kind permission of publishers Victor Gollancz Ltd, London.

Figures 1.2 and 1.3 are based upon material in Barrett 1991, with the permission of the author and as orginally sourced from Japan Minister of the Environment and OECD/IEA. See: Barrett, B 1991 Japan and the global environment: A case for leadership. *Japan Digest* (UK), July 1991: 29–35.

Some materials used in the study of Kansai airport are drawn from B Barrett and R Therivel 1991, *Environmental Policy and Impact Assessment in Japan*, London: Routledge, with the permission of the authors and publisher.

The case studies concerning (1) audit of a chemical production facility and (2) a waste transfer station in Chapter 4, are drawn from articles originally appearing in the UK journal *Environment Business–Environmental Auditing Supplement* (Summer 1991). The material is reproduced and adapted with the kind permission of Travers Morgan Environmental, East Grinstead (chemical plant) and M J Carter Associated (waste transfer station) and for information from Mr Alistair Bailee.

Material concerning the Oxfordshire County Council case study of environmental audit, Chapter 6, is based upon a talk by John Harwood, Chief Executive, and is used with his permission.

Material and quotations taken from National Trust environmental audit study is based on work by R Jarman, and is used with the permission of the author.

Appendix A is quoted from the US Environmental Protection Agency's document *Environmental Auditing Policy Statement* (1986).

Appendix B, Matters for Environmental Assessment, is taken by kind permission of the Controller of Her Majesty's Stationery Office from: *Environmental Assessment: A Guide to Procedures*, Department of the Environment.

Appendix C is based on a report by the US Geological Survey (Leopold et al., 1971) and on the UK Dept. of the Environment's 1989 booklet *Environmental Assessment: A Guide to the Procedures*.

Grant Ledgerwood, University of Greenwich
Elizabeth Street, Kent County Council
Riki Therivel, Oxford Polytechnic

INTRODUCTION

'Businesses made a great deal of money fouling the
world over the last 200 years. I have no doubt that
there are many fortunes to be made cleaning things
up over the next three generations.'
*Sir Crispin Tickell, speaking at the annual conference of
the Institute of Directors, London, March 1991*

This book gives managers tools to help them lead their firms towards
compliance with environmental regulations, and towards a green strategy
integrated into the whole of corporate culture. It reviews recent international changes in environmental legislation and public expectations. It
shows how these changes are transforming corporate priorities for the
next decade and beyond. It reviews techniques for developing managers'
capabilities in environmental assessment, audit and corporate monitoring. Throughout, it emphasises the application of total quality
management to all aspects of the corporate environmental programme.

A principal purpose of this text is to assist managers in mounting an
operational corporate environmental programme, and in seeing how
such a programme relates to the processes of negotiating change in the
organisation. The environmental manager will increasingly be asked to
give advice to senior managers on questions of new business development, acquisition and disposal. Thus this text aims to give an understanding of corporate decision-making concerning business selection and
development.

Environmental strategy needs to encompass:

- legal requirements, which may go above minimal compliance;
- potential environmental liability, which impinges on the company's
  financial viability, insurance programme and market valuation;
- the company's perceived responsibility and broader public expecta-

tion, which will condition the reception of the company's presence, products and services in its marketplaces.

Clearly these areas impinge on each other. To serve only the first is to be reacting, not proacting. Full strategic assimilation of environmental issues means that every aspect of the company's past, present and future plant, processes and products must be systematically and repeatedly subjected to environmental assessment and audit.

This book does not aim to provide the technical depth required for environmental audit. Indeed, a large enterprise will require considerable external and internal expertise, and several years' investment, to develop a corporate environmental programme. Instead, this book will prepare the manager coming into a relevant and responsible role for devising and/or implementing a corporate environmental programme to ask the right questions of his or her consultants and staff, and to structure a process of audit, assessment, control and monitoring of environmental impacts. Moreover, it will equip the manager to understand the inter-connections between environmental strategies and other strategies in the corporate environment – product, marketing, human resourcing.

The book is thus a starting point for those without an extensive environmental background. In that respect, it does not seek to cover many technical issues: for instance, there are no prolonged discussions of complex chemical interactions between various gaseous pollutants coming from a factory; nor is there any ambition to satisfy the complex drafting problems surrounding the environmental labelling of products. The aim is to equip the environmental manager with tools by which the totality of environmental strategies can be managed from the perspective of Total Quality Management.

Part I of the book reviews the pressures building up from consumers, from the regulatory, scientific and investment communities, and from stakeholders in business and government. It provides a synopsis of key methods for carrying out environmental audit and assessment and shows how managers can introduce corporate environmental programmes in their own organisations. Techniques from the fields of innovation management and management of change are linked to environmental strategy-making. It shows how a company's environmental agenda can be developed to assist the development of successful business strategies.

Part II is centred on a detailed procedure for establishing and executing an environmental audit. It is aimed at the general manager coming into environmental responsibilities. The emphasis is on precise and compre-

comprehensive communications within the organisation and with the various stakeholders outside its walls.

Part III takes this emphasis further by considering at each stage the quality dimensions of corporate environmental programmes. Total Quality Management is presented as a model of co-responsibility for compliance with environmental codes. Rather than there being a post-operations audit with its potential terrors of discovery and penalty, Total Quality Management aims at quality immersion and commitment from every member of the team from the front end of production. Thus, training and motivation strategies are central to Total Quality Management in the corporate environmental programme.

This orientation for the first time fuses recent developments in behavioural models of corporate management, of which Total Quality Management is one of the most current (see, e.g., Wille, 1992). Rather than establishing a normative model of environmental management, the organisation must work with the people and practices it inherits. Much of the improvements in a company's environmental performance will come from a patient and long-term inculcation of the environmental message into each activity.

Finally, a word is needed about word usage. In this text, the term 'audit' is used to encompass both environmental audit and environmental assessment procedures. Environmental audit has evolved from financial audit, where similar problems arise. The term environmental assessment is used specifically to mean an audit of major proposed projects and their likely changes to the environment: it entails predictions of future events, and thus generally involves greater uncertainty than an audit of an existing operation. Part II proposes a protocol which encompasses both procedures generically.

PART I

Business and the Environment: Regulation and Management Systems Since 1960

Part I places business and corporate environmental strategy in the context of the radical changes in national and international perceptions of the environment dating from the early 1960s. Chapter 1 reviews historically and regionally different approaches and key experiences which have influenced national and regional co-ordination of business and environmental impacts.

Chapter 2 reflects on a number of key business cases, together with episodes of pollution and ecological disaster. These incidents have triggered public reaction and consequent environmental legislation. But they also influenced the development of new approaches to international investment and to the problems of industrial and business liability insurance.

Chapter 3 considers some of the key conceptual systems used in corporate management. It proposes a model of corporate management of environmental audit, to adapt it through the application of the precepts of Total Quality Management to normative concepts of best environmental performance.

I THE NEW ENVIRONMENTAL REGULATION FRAMEWORK: ORIGINS AND CONSEQUENCES FOR BUSINESS STRATEGY

The origins – economic, political and cultural – of environmental regulation are complex. Environmental audit is a new element in corporate strategy. It is the natural outcome of a growing environmental awareness which began in the 1960s and has culminated in the 1990s with the understanding that it is the responsibility of every firm and individual to contribute towards the solution of global environmental issues. For these reasons it must be seen as an area of business innovation, requiring the skills of change management as it is being adopted within the corporate setting. Figure 1-1 shows key points of this global environmental movement.

A NEW CONSENSUS

Since the early 1960s, increasing scientific and political attention has been paid to conflicts between economic growth and the natural environment. The first surge of this new awareness came in the late 1960s and early 1970s; it was exemplified by the establishment of the US Environmental Protection Agency, victorious lawsuits by Japanese victims of heavy metal poisoning and a spate of new environmental laws internationally. Since the mid 1980s a second worldwide phase of environmental awareness has resulted in many changes to the laws governing the interactions between business and the environment.

A consensus is emerging regarding the need to pursue both economic growth and environmental sustainability. Indeed, economic development without sustainability is self-defeating and leads to disaster. Without the environmental support system no economy is possible. Increasingly both governments and communities expect that industry will minimise or eradicate adverse impacts on its surroundings. Communities

1960

1962   Publication of Rachel Carson's *Silent Spring*; Global problems with insecticides

1970

1972   US National Environmental Protection Act; formation of National Environmental Protection Agency

1972   First Earth Day

1972   First Earth Summit; formation of United Nations Environmental Agency

1974   First energy crisis

1975   OECD establishes principle of 'polluter pays'

1974–5   Energy conservation becomes major international political issue for first time

1975   US federal law requires environmental assessment of federal projects

1976   Cloud of trichlorphenol vapour spreads through Seveso area of Italy

1980

early 1980s on   Environmental audit carried out by many large companies

1983   Further dioxin release at Seveso, Italy

1983   Greenpeace and Friends of the Earth develop public confrontation and symbolic confrontation strategies to capture public awareness in, e.g. whale conservation issues

1984   Bhopal India: major escape of toxic fumes kills 4,000, injures tens of thousands

1985   European Commission agrees first environmental assessment regulation

1985   Environmental audit becomes part of acquisition and disposal procedure in North America

1986   Chernobyl nuclear power plant disaster

1987   Single European Act 1986: first American environmental audit regulation

late 1980s on   'Deep green' eco-guerilla movement, western USA

1987   Publication of Brundtland Report, entrenching sustainable development as key strategic dimension in environmental policy

1988   Implementation across Europe of Environmental Assessment Directive

1990   Principle of integrated pollution control in United Kingdom Environmental Protection Act

1990   Defeat of California 'big green' environmental legislation; local adoption of many aspects

1991   Proposal for European Environmental Agency

1991   Draft Eco-Audit Directive, Europe

1992   In opposition to local environmental regulation, many California companies in deep recession threaten removal to less regulated states

1992   GATT publishes report on world free trade and environmental issues

1992   Second Earth Summit of UN in Rio de Janeiro

1990

Source: Environmental Assessment Group, Kent County Council; EcoCommunity Programme IMRIC U of Greenwich

Figure 1.1   The global environmental movement: points on the pathway

are no longer content to accept pollution as the necessary cost for generating employment and trade.

Thus, in the last decade of the 20th century, economic development is seen as a mixed blessing. Development can damage both human health and the planet's capacity for self-regeneration. Growth must be channelled and directed, designed and limited, if it is to produce viable industries which can serve society over the coming centuries. The earth itself is seen as fragile and finite, rather than the untamable wilderness which it was still perceived to be as recently as the First World War. Most of all, the international business community itself is now beginning to address its responsibilities in ensuring that the environment in which it functions can sustain change and accommodate growth.

IMPLICATIONS FOR BUSINESS AND MANAGEMENT

Over the next decade, these changes are likely to have a major effect on the way that organisations manage their plant and products. Companies will be required to take responsibility for the pollution and wastes they cause, and for the future recycling of their products, and none of this responsibility will be allowed to be sold downstream. In many countries, companies are already required to take responsibility for, and minimise, their impacts on the environment. For the first time, company strategies will have to take a comprehensive environmental stance towards product lifecycles and production operations.

Industry itself has proven that recycling waste products and mitigating pollution is associated with high-profit, long-term business development. Such high-growth international firms as Apple Computers, Nike Sports Clothing, Shell, the UK household products group Reckitt and Colman, and IBM have increasingly made environmental goals part of their over-all corporate philosophy and plans. Managers are rewarded for achieving environmental as well as financial and other targets.

On the other hand, many firms are not yet vigorously outspoken about their environmental programmes, because not many firms have yet achieved a very high level of environmental protection. Most major companies in the advanced industrial world carried out environmental audit as a voluntary step during the late 1980s, but few found that their environmental records were so outstanding that they wished to make their audits public.

However, these companies are now laying the groundwork for future success in their environmental and corporate settings. For as they progressively replace outmoded plant and unfriendly products with environmentally better choices, these investments can be made public and can thus enhance the attractiveness of the business to investors and to local communities. In addition, of course, the corporation reduces the likelihood of being charged with criminal pollution or the production of hazardous products – disasters which have in a few cases affected major firms in recent decades. The cases of Johns Manville (USA – asbestos), Lloyd's of London (UK – diverse insurance claims, many pollution-linked), and Union Carbide (USA and India – factory explosion; now recovering) are prominent.

Because of environmental legislation, the investment and insurance industries are altering their approach to business valuation. Investment strategies in buying companies, investing in company stocks and projecting potential insurance liabilities are incorporating new guidelines. Corporations which have adopted the full range of environmental requirements and are moving rapidly towards the adoption of a full 'green' agenda will be in a good position, as markets and consumers will increasingly favour such companies.

Government operations will also be comprehensively affected. Politicians have discovered that the consequences of wholesale major change, through new projects – dams, power plants, motorways, slum clearance and the like – have included environmental damage as well as economic growth. These must be audited, and negative impacts must be mitigated, as part of the public sector's commitment towards solving the global environmental crisis.

Scientists have grown more aware of the environmental implications of their work. New applications for science, such as biotechnology, have meant that the potential for environmental damage has also increased.

The cumulative effect of these changes is that every public or private corporation in the developed world will within a decade be required to be thoroughly 'green' in strategy and operation, and a similar but slower trend is expected in the developing world. It is only by setting good practice that industry and government in the wealthy nations can hope to influence the dynamic growth economies of the developing world to take better care of the environment than has hitherto been the case in Europe.

For the manager in business and government over coming decades, a new view of business growth and general economic increase will be necessary. Company growth is possible, but in a way which older managers would find limiting. Yet clear signals are evident that industry and research institutions are responding with sustainable technologies and products with recycling capabilities.

Therefore, what can be called the environmental agenda will be assiduously structured into corporate planning and development, alongside financial and human resources, marketing and other major functional aspects of business management. Not to do so courts major legal and financial hazards, as well as substantial loss of consumer good-will. No successful business can therefore avoid environmental policy.

THE DEVELOPMENT OF ENVIRONMENTAL LEGISLATION

North America

North America, including Canada, has, since the early 1970s, led the field in environmental audit and control methods and regulations. The reasons for this early public awareness and pioneering legislation relate to their historically wealthier economies, their socio-political systems and their resource bases.

Richer societies aspire to higher levels of environmental well-being. Because of their wealth, rich countries are able to afford to maintain their higher living standards as they also incorporate the costs of product purification, wildlife conservation, landscape reclamation, pollution control and waste recycling into their economies. Put another way, the costs of rapid growth are often at the expense of the natural environment. As consumers and producers become aware of these costs, they are able to choose to reduce or eliminate negative environmental impacts by paying higher prices. Some economic growth becomes expressed in environmental industries, which themselves become part of the expanding world economy.

In North America the environment has been heavily polluted during the relatively short period of industrialisation since the 19th century. Severe pollution has always affected fairly large and heavily industrial centres of populations such as Pittsburgh and Cleveland. However, because the net population density of North America is only about $\frac{1}{10}$ as great as, for instance, that of southern England or northern Germany, the consequences of heavy pollution have only recently begun to be seen as capable of being altered without loss of economic viability.

The wealth of resources on the North American continent, and the shock of discovering their finiteness, influenced the early development of environmental legislation. In many cases it had been traditional for large companies to exploit resources in a particular region, 'stripping' out timber, coal, fish, aluminium, copper, nickel or uranium. The tailings were dumped at random in the landscape, leaving large tracts of wilderness and forest denuded or polluted. Waste water was poured into river basins and groundwater reservoirs, destroying watersheds and river life for hundreds of miles. All this was justified in the name of jobs, progress and economic growth.

With the closing of the frontier between about 1910 and 1930, the national mentality changed. The native North American landscape was increasingly seen as tamed, threatened and requiring protection, and the tradition of large-scale resource exploitation became increasingly associated with lawlessness in industrial life. Public sentiment against the great 'Trusts' in coal, steel, oil and railroads rejected both their capacity to destroy whole towns through monopoly practices and also, later, their ability to disfigure and pollute the environment. Rather than enhancing the American way, environmental degradation has become like an attack against the flag, identified with disloyalty and lack of patriotism.

With the formation of the first national parks in the 1870s, the American conservation movement established a procedure for imposing national legislation on the workings of the free enterprise system. The environment and its accessibility to the American public were seen to be inextricably linked to traditions of local responsibility, the pioneer mentality and the shared experience of dramatic landscapes. Although there was no established religion in the American constitution, the natural environment became a common spiritual link between diverse regions, traditions and climates. The need for environmental protection was voiced particularly clearly in Rachel Carson's *Silent Spring* (1962).

These movements were quickly reflected in Canada, and later in Europe. What had been taken for granted – the inherent robustness and infinite capacity of nature, and man's inbuilt right to assault his economy into her – was now seen as threatened. For the first time, business was seen to be potentially against some of society's fundamental values.

It was the long tradition of national sentiment and love for the American landscape and wilderness which first gave rise to the environmental legislation of the last third of the 20th century. American corporations have had difficulty in meeting their voluntary objectives in such areas as urban renewal and improved minority job opportunities.

However, there is broad and deep agreement within and outside the business community that the physical environment itself, shared and needed by all, must be given priority if economic well-being is to be sustainable over the long term.

Other important political and cultural characteristics shared by both the American and Canadian societies have influenced their relatively early adoption of environmental control over business. In political terms, the US and Canada are federal states, with much of their power decentralised to state, provincial and local government. This is particularly true in land planning and urban development. The low population densities of North America and the wide traditions of local home rule, embedded in constitution and tradition, have made it relatively difficult to establish national systems of environmental control, unlike in Europe. The willingness to legislate reflects the lack of any other national land planning policy in these very large federal states, with strong regional governments jealous of their territorial responsibilities. Control over industrial and urban development differs radically among different provinces and states. The environmental cause allowed for a national solution to the lack of land planning control. Therefore, a consensus built up around interstate and interprovincial resource dimensions – air quality, the quality of surface and groundwater, soil quality and the prevention of erosion.

As a result of the initial years of the environmental movement and rising concern over the environmental effects of industrial and technological applications without assessment of their potential harm, the US Congress passed the National Environmental Policy Act (NEPA) in 1969. This requires that the impacts of proposed major projects are predicted and mitigated against. From then on, the US and Canada established that care of the environment was a legal concern of the national state. Importantly, this concern overrode the states' rights of separate powers, embedded in the American Constitution. Similarly in the Canadian federal system, provinces were required to recognise the federal government's overriding responsibilities for the well-being of the entire habitat, crossing all internal boundaries.

Since then there has been increasing international co-operation between the two countries on such issues as acid rain, timber conservation, fishery resources, undersea minerals extraction and conservation, and water resources. This last item has been especially important, as it affects the Great Lakes, the St Lawrence River, and the Pacific coast waters of Puget Sound. Equally important was the 'energy crisis' of the 1970s, in which the withdrawal of cheap petroleum brought about a conviction that energy efficiency was a paramount goal in order to decrease dependence on imports.

The US Environmental Protection Agency endorsed the concept of environmental auditing in a policy statement of July 1986. The statement (reproduced in Appendix A of this book) focused on the use of auditing at federal facilities, and its relationship to state and local regulatory agencies. The application of voluntary environmental auditing in the US has meant that plants, through self-assessment of production methods, and of factory management and organisation, are able to check that they maintain compliance with environmental codes.

The continued development of environmental politics in America has been spearheaded by such organisations as the Sierra Club. In contrast with this 'do-gooder' form of activism, eco-guerrillaism – using covert, sometimes violent, often illegal tactics against polluters and environmental degraders – has been seen in western states and provinces since the mid 1970s. Small groups of political activists have used sabotage and acts of civil disobedience to prevent environmental disruption. Internationally, Greenpeace has engineered carefully controlled confrontations with their opponents, to focus media attention on particularly abhorrent environmental problems. Extra-legal groups have continued to challenge the legal system.

In California in 1990, an attempt was made to give regulatory form to the concerns of the most militant of environmental groups, now reaching across many of the cities. A major package of environmental controls, referred to popularly as 'Big Green', was placed before the California electorate as a referendum. While the issue failed to gain a majority, it provides a view of the increasingly severe constraints which technology, industry and urban development will have to meet in the 1990s in order to lead, rather than follow, popular and electoral demands.

In Canada, with its less militant traditions, there yet remain severe demands that resource extraction, the driving force of the national economy, be allied closely to conservation. For the nation as a whole the natural environment is linked to a sense of national identity and to Canada's distinctive political cultures.

Europe

North-west Europe has had a dense urban population, and severe slum and pollution problems for over a century. For this reason, environmental control in the form of environmental health regulations and town and country planning legislation has been in place for longer than in North America. Prior to the environmental legislation of recent decades, north-west European states – in particular the UK, Germany, France, Denmark and The Netherlands – had extensive air quality and land planning controls in place. These controls had to some extent limited industrial emissions, conflicting land uses, deposition of toxic waste and other environmental problems.

By the 1980s, Europe's affluence had led to increasing demands for motorways and other forms of infrastructure, as well as increasing public requirements for higher environmental quality. These trends led to the adoption of an environmental agenda in politics. In northern Europe during the 1980s the Green parties played major roles in establishing new political priorities in national legislative councils. As political leaders understood and adopted environmental concerns as their own, they put into place in most countries partial and increasingly comprehensive regulatory regimes which penalise polluters. In most cases, the installation of mitigating technology has been assisted through tax credits.

Generally, however, the initial response within western European states to the environmental agenda has been muted. Several reasons account for this slower application. European planning law, at least in north-western Europe, already required a measure of environmental assessment as part of normal planning and development controls. Corporate and government actors had also already found means of controlling chemical and nuclear toxic wastes in response to the existing requirements of occupational health laws, the social welfare culture and the high density of population. The problems of regaining economic growth have also tended, until recent years, to swamp environmental issues.

In the absence of clear national environmental commitments, the Commission of the European Communities (EC) has taken the initiative in setting an environmental agenda for its Member States. The Single European Act of 1987 explicitly identified environmental measures as appropriate to the work of the EC. Member States are allowed to adopt more stringent protective measures than those adopted by the Council of Ministers, as long as they are consistent with the Act (Owen and Mundy, 1991).

In 1985 the EC adopted its first Directive requiring Member States to carry out environmental assessment of major projects. Similar to North American practice, considerable local variation in the techniques of implementation has been permitted, reflecting the diverse nature of European legal and business settings.

By 1991 there were over 80 Directives and other EC proposals for environmental regulation. A European Environment Agency was proposed, with the objective of providing scientific and technical knowledge regarding environmental protection both to the Community and to Member States.

In the summer of 1991 a draft EC 'Directive for Civil Liability for Damage caused by Waste' was published as the pivotal Directive around which all further environmental Directives will be focused (*Financial Times*, 9 October 1991). The draft proposed two key features which had previously been developed in American and Japanese courts:

- The legal principle of strict liability in environmental regulation. This means that the plaintiff would not have to prove either negligence or causation on the part of the defendant in order to start court proceedings.
- The 'polluter pays' principle. Stemming from an OECD statement of the early 1970s, this legal principle would make any originator of pollution responsible for its ultimate treatment and disposal, no matter how remote it was from the source.

Two further points are being structured into this Directive:

- Primary liability is to be extended to carriers as well as producers of waste.
- Public interest voluntary groups – for instance Greenpeace or Friends of the Earth – will have the power to initiate court actions with fewer restrictions.

The draft Directive also argues for compulsory insurance programmes, which in 1991 showed considerable variation among Member States. Although definitive in many areas, this draft legislation leaves many questions open to adjudication over the coming years. For instance, the extent of retroactive liability for industrial pollution damage has not yet been made clear. Such liability will have to be arrived at through both application of legal principles in the continental tradition and the development of case law as in British jurisprudence.

In 1991 a draft EC Code for Environmental Audit (eco-audit) was being developed. Eco-audit is of particular relevance to the nuclear industry, which produces about 20 per cent of European electricity in the early 1990s. The impact of the Chernobyl nuclear disaster in 1987 brought home to western Europe that the custodians of nuclear industry may be unable to control a catastrophic plant meltdown.

At the same time, the British Standards Institution has adopted its own environmental management system, which uses a cradle-to-grave approach to environmental resources and implies the need for regular environmental auditing. The proposed system requires companies to ensure that their activities comply with environmental legislation and regulations. If standards are not met, fines may be levied or, more significantly, heavier insurance premiums may be imposed by the private market. Eco-audit and the environmental management system are discussed at length in Chapter 5.

Future EC measures are likely to include control of municipal waste water and hazardous waste; civil liability for damage and environmental degradation caused by waste; the classification, packaging and labelling of products; and the control of vehicle emissions. There are further proposals for economic and physical instruments to deliver EC environmental programmes.

Implementing the EC's integrated approach to the environment, focusing on pollution control and heavy industry, the UK's Environmental Protection Act of 1990 introduced 'integrated pollution control' (IPC). IPC is a single procedure of assessment which aims to minimise the total impacts on the environment of all releases and emissions from a given plant, including those to air, water and land. This means that for project planning in any industry targeted for IPC, environmental protection automatically becomes a key corporate strategic objective, and not a peripheral issue brought late to the agenda.

Under s.7 of the Environmental Protection Act 1990, before Her Majesty's Inspector of Pollution can grant authorisations it must ensure that developers use the concepts of BATNEEC and BPEO. BATNEEC stands for 'best available techniques not entailing excessive costs'. BPEO stands for 'best practicable environmental option', which refers to the choice as to which part of the environment – water, air or land – is best suited to take a release of pollution: it is the assessment of which part of the environment in a particular case should be 'polluted'.

Both BATNEEC and BPEO involve a balancing of economic and environmental elements, which means knowing environmental and economic costs. It therefore follows that firms that are affected by the Environmental Protection Act 1990 will have gone some way towards completing an environmental audit. In obtaining authorisation under Part I of the Environmental Protection Act 1990, companies will be gathering information about environmental benefits as part of the obligatory process of gaining IPC authorisation.

Integrated pollution control is already pushing firms in the direction of providing well-managed information-gathering procedures relating to environmental impacts. It is then only a small additional increment to begin a comprehensive procedure for analysing environmental impacts. Such analysis will clearly be the main element of a general purpose environmental audit. Existing legislation enables European firms to consider current performance in terms of medium-term goals. Once a company's current environmental performance has been established, it can begin to make necessary changes at its own pace. If firms wait for external events to force the pace, they will not be able to direct change. Instead change will direct companies.

Advice from impending EC legislation is thus to implement environmental auditing now. Companies have probably already been doing much of this work so as to achieve compliance with environmental regulations, satisfy bank lenders or get the best price for the assets being sold. An environmental balance sheet will be obligatory in the near future for a loan or to obtain insurance on good terms.

Thus, in a few years environmental issues have gone from the marginal political concerns of small 'Green' parties in various European countries into the core legal and investment requirements imposed on larger industries throughout the EC. Certainly many industrialists and political leaders see a competitive advantage for their own sectors in attaining a lead in eco-audit technology and compliance.

It is no coincidence that by the early part of the 1990s most of the large American and British law firms had opened environmental offices in Brussels, alongside their French, German and other partners. In environmental law, more than in any other area of legislation, the EC is expected to make substantial inroads across national boundaries in coming years.

Japan

Japan, like the north-west European countries, has very high population densities. Nuclear bombs brought home to the Japanese nation the consequences of technology allowed to go out of control as thousands still continue to suffer premature death from the consequences of nuclear fallout, four decades after the end of the Second World War.

During the 1960s, Japanese people in Minamata and Nigata suffered from mercury poisoning after eating polluted fish drawn from coastal waters. Similarly, people in Toyama prefecture were poisoned by cadmium discharged into the local river by a smelting company. None the less, during the 1960s and 1970s the Tokyo metropolitan area, some 60 miles across, was allowed to develop without planning controls in the western sense. The imperative of economic recovery dominated all other values until the 1970s. The vast urban region is still plagued by chronic traffic congestion, high levels of air and water pollution, and conflicts between industrial and residential land uses which will take decades to resolve.

As a result of the oil shocks of the 1970s, coupled with vigourous public concern, Japan had achieved by the early 1990s one of the most rigorous pollution control systems in the world. Japan's production of carbon dioxide (CO_2) is now less per capita than that of most of the US, Germany, the UK, Canada and Sweden. Sulphur dioxide (SO_2) and nitrogen oxide (NO_x) production per capita is also less (OECD, 1991). The oil shocks also had major benefits in energy conservation. According to the OECD, only the UK has been more successful in reducing its energy costs per unit of GDP: in 1988, Japan used 69 per cent as much energy per unit of GDP as in 1970, while the UK used 67 per cent as much. The key to this success has been the use of technological measures, rather than demand suppression, to reduce pollution. These technologies are now available for export.

	1970	1980	1988
USA	100	88	73
Japan	100	84	69
France	100	92	84
Germany (W)	100	89	77
Italy	100	87	77
Netherlands	100	98	87
Sweden	100	90	89
UK	100	80	67

Figure 1.2   Trends in Energy Requirements by unit of GDP (1970 = 100)
Source: OECD/IEA; as quoted by Barrett, 1991.

However, this progress has not been altogether without resistance. After a period of strong environmental concern and effective environmental regulations in the 1970s, little new legislation emerged until the late 1980s. Air quality, although better than 20 years ago, is now deteriorating in the large conurbations. Until recently, Japan was still causing severe environmental depredations: exploitation of rain forests in the Asia–Pacific region, illegal import of ivory and other wildlife products, drift-net fishing in the Pacific, and whaling in the Antarctic and Pacific.

As in Europe, high land values and high population densities conflict with rising public expectations about an amenable and healthy urban environment. More importantly, there is now public acceptance by political leaders that Japan, because of its huge manufacturing output, is a major contributor to greenhouse gases, deforestation and the deterioration of water quality.

In the 1990s a key issue has become whether Japan should use its enormous economic well-being to develop a national and international environmental strategy, both in regulation and technology (see Barrett, 1991; Barrett and Therivel, 1991). Another issue is whether Japan will use its powerful combination of economic and technological leadership to establish global leadership in environmental management. Such leadership has been targeted by industrial and political leaders (Maruyama, 1991).

Japan has many proposals and plans for technological and industrial developments in the environmental field. The Ministry of International Trade and Industry (MITI), which is the major Japanese centre for future economic and technology studies, has now published an action programme called 'New Earth 21', which is outlined in Figure 1.3. This is expected to combat global warming over the next hundred years. Its elements include energy conservation strategies, clean energy sourcing, new technologies for pollution and production and, most strikingly, an ambitious plan for the enlargement and enhancement of CO_2 sinks, both in the oceans and the forest. These would function across the global landscape.

This strategy would, if successful, replicate the previous industrial success of Japan. First, specific new products would be developed to cater for expanding home markets: in this case the demand would be for pollution-free, high-quality urban technologies which offer the jobs and transport facilities on which national prosperity rests. Secondly, these products would be developed by competing corporations with increasing design and marketing sophistication for sale into competitive home markets, ensuring that less successful products get squeezed out. Finally, the most successful manufacturers would take their highly refined product ranges into export markets, where they could be targeted at dissatisfied consumers whose home producers offered only narrow and inadequate choices.

Year 1990 2000 2010 2020 2030 2040 2050 2060 2070 2080 2090

• Intensified scientific research to reduce uncertainties
• Accelerated energy conservation   World energy conservation
• CFCs phased out   programme

    • Safer nuclear plants   Accelerated introduction of clean energy
       • New and renewable energy sources

     • Third generation CFC substitutes   Development of environment-
     • CO_2 fixation and re-utilisation technology   friendly technology
        • Environment-friendly production processes
• Reforestation   ➡

     • Reversing desertification through biotechnology
       (plants resistant to salt and drought)   Enhancing CO_2 sinks
        • Enhancing oceanic skills

➡

     • Nuclear fusion   Development of future
     • Space solar power generation   energy technology

Source: Adapted from Barrett, 1991

Figure 1.3 Japan's global environmental programme

Japan's successful international construction industry has also undertaken a number of recent studies showing how development can improve
the global environment. For example, the Shimizu Corporation has produced the 'Desert Aqua-Net Plan'. This proposes the creation of huge
artificial lakes in desert areas, which would become centres for fishing,
ocean farming and water recreation. The lakes would be 40km in dia-
meter and connected by a series of transportation canals. An extension of
this is the Obayashi Corporation's plans for 'Mars Habitation 1' in the
year 2057, the first planned human settlement on Mars.

Japanese business has increasingly focused on new products with
environmental standards. In 1987 the Environment Agency introduced
the first national 'Eco-Mark', a voluntary scheme for environmentally
friendly goods. By the early 1990s some 30 ranges of goods could be
registered and branded under this scheme.

Japan is also influencing global deliberations on environmental policy.
In June 1989 the country's Council of Ministers for Global Environment
Conservation adopted six policy guidelines:

1 Japan resolves to lead the international drive to protect the global environment and to co-operate with other nations to solve its problems.
2 Japan's experts will monitor and research the domestic and global environments and share information with foreign experts.
3 Japan will promote the development of environment-friendly technologies.
4 Japan will support environmental protection efforts in developing countries.
5 Japan will take into account the environmental protection policies of the candidate when allocating official development assistance.
6 Japan will continuously educate its population on ways to lessen the strain their economy places on the global environment. (*Quoted in Barrett, 1991*)

These changes are reflected in the rapid increases in the Environment Agency's budget, which grew roughly four times between 1989 and 1991 ($750 million to $3 billion, approximately). Much of this money is dedicated to energy conservation research and development. Substantial amounts also go to the United Nations Environment Programme (UNEP), World Health Organisation (WHO), and the Convention on International Trade in Endangered Species (CITES). There are increasing pressures for overseas development assistance funds to be linked to environmental issues.

The optimism of these and many other related proposals suggests the underlying assumption built deeply into Japanese business: global development can carry on without disastrous consequences, if the appropriate technology is available. Improvements in global conditions are expected in the foreseeable future. These values and assumptions might be challenged by many 'deep green' environmentalists in the West, as well as by scientists concerned with the CO_2 increases.

There are, however, notable gaps in these strategies. While energy conservation is emphasised, overall global resource conservation is ignored. Despite large recent increases in development aid, Japan tends to tread around issues of inequalities of resources and income between developing and industrialised nations. These are issues which Japan may well have addressed by the mid 1990s, however.

Similarly, although the Japanese public has become more environmentally aware in recent years, there is still not the broad-based public activism which has been characteristic of North America and Europe. Whereas public concern has forced Western governments to adopt a more active environmental role, in Japan the tendency has been for government to be in advance of the public. Thus, one finds the Japanese Environmental Agency using television to draw the attention of mass audiences to negative trends in air and water pollution in the late 1980s. Without mass public support, increased restrictions on manufacturers and producers would be difficult.

As Barrett (1991) points out, the West has neither the surplus capital nor the intellectual and business energy to work towards global environmental reclamation as energetically as some of the Japanese consortia are doing. The Japanese system has relied on the American military umbrella and is notably weak in armaments. However, the Japanese politico-industrial complex now leads the world in its capacity to design and market high-technology products in a wide range of fields.

> Japan's global leadership in environmental management puts a priority on policies and technologies which emphasise Japan's pacifism . . . [I]t could reflect its emergence as a leader dedicated to solving global environmental problems in co-operation with all nations (*Barrett, 1991*).

The stakes are thus very large. To continue to be prosperous, Japan needs a stable international system of trading partners which cannot be achieved by force. Nor is economic acquisition in overseas countries a major alternative, for this will be resisted if it is seen to infringe on core sovereignty (Vernon, 1971). Only through an international co-operative system of free trade, within a global environment managed in a sustainable manner, can this be achieved. Japan may be well suited to provided some of the leadership required for this challenge over the next century.

Developing countries

The very poorest countries, such as some Central and West African nations, have suffered greatly in recent years from the loss in value of their key cash crops, as the price of agricultural commodities steadily dropped during the 1980s. For this reason, their governments are agreeing in some cases to accept exploitatively underpriced mining deals, sites for the disposal of toxic wastes and recycling plants which are being refused planning permission in advanced industrial countries.

For instance, Sierra Leone in West Africa has a rich alluvial base and the capacity for agricultural self-sufficiency and export. None the less in recent years its cash crops have proven unsuccessful. Mining companies from Europe have been able to impose underpriced contracts which sterilise large tracts of agricultural area and toxic wastes are being deposited without proper safeguards.

These practices will increasingly be reviewed by the United Nations and eventually by the General Agreement on Tariffs and Trade (GATT), the international treaty organisation governing global trade relationships. Political sentiment in the West will eventually refuse to accept that toxic wastes should be exported from their countries to Third World countries. Increasingly, both nations and industries will be required to account for and fully process their wastes.

Brazil, which is now among the top dozen largest industrial economies in the world, offers a contrasting example. Its great industrial and business centres, focused around São Paolo and Rio de Janeiro, host a number of leading multinational financial and industrial groups which will increasingly play a lead role in Latin American development. European and North American concern about the loss of the rain forests, as well as about the misery of the slums of this energetic nation of enormous resources and space, is being matched by a rising middle-class concern within Brazil. The current government is as fully focused on environmental policy as many advanced-economy governments.

SUPRANATIONAL AUTHORITIES AND AGREEMENTS

The environmental sphere is a natural 'habitat' for supranational authorities such as the European Commission, the International Maritime Organisation, the World Health Organisation, the United National Environmental Agency and the World Bank. This section discusses two examples, those of the Brundtland Commission and of GATT, but many other similar authorities exist.

The Brundtland Commission

The Norwegian prime minister and a prominent panel of world statesmen, on behalf of UNEP, examined international and global policy within a developmental context. Her commission, reporting in 1987, brought a wide international response. The commission indicated that global pollution control and economic development in the Third World are potentially in conflict. Thus, the concept of finding a method and level of development which could be sustained indefinitely without environmental damage was emphasised in improving global environmental policy. Economic development and social mobility must be accompanied by environmental protection. This consensus provided a basis for a major reshaping of economic development theory, as Pearce and others (1989a) have demonstrated.

Following the world reception of the Brundtland Report, investors have paid more attention to corporate impacts on sustainability impacts. The influence of ethics and the concept of ethical investment has been linked to environmental protection. Other social concerns have been targeted as rising issues of international business ethics, such as women's rights, children's labour, animal rights and the problems of ethnic minorities. But, overwhelmingly, the ethical investment industry has focused on environmental protection, because clearly here lie issues which simultaneously link ethical considerations with longer-term sustainability of a business and its stakeholders.

GATT and international trade

Since the 1950s the GATT has been a major facilitating mechanism to the huge increase in world trade. The potential conflict between GATT's economic and environmental objectives became crystallised in 1991 with the emergence of controversy concerning environmental regulations which were seen as preventing free competition among the trading enterprises of different nations.

GATT practices give trade law a higher priority than environmental and other legislation, including employment relations, and industrial and safety law. Fundamentally it was argued that more stringent environmental regulations in one country – recycling, energy management and so on – disadvantaged would-be importing countries from abroad who could not easily trade into the more highly regulated setting (*Financial Times*, 18 September 1991).

In 1990 the EC dismissed Denmark's recycled container laws as contrary to free trade, and similar German legislation is being subjected to threats of this kind. In 1991 a dispute settlement panel ruled in favour of Mexico after the US imposed restrictions on Mexico's tuna imports on the grounds that Mexican fishing nets also killed dolphins. So severe was the controversy that in September 1991 members of the US Senate proposed the creation of an environmental code in the GATT international code. This was modelled on the current GATT subsidies code.

Increasingly it was seen that GATT would need to be fundamentally changed if the overriding priorities of environmental policies were to be fulfilled. Clearly any environmental regulation could be challenged as 'anti-competitive' by any country which chose not so to regulate. The proposed environmental code would allow each nation to set its own environmental standards in all product areas. Three criteria would be required of these standards:

- they must be judged to have a sound scientific basis;
- the same standards must be applied to all competitive domestic production;
- imported products must be judged to be causing economic injury to competing domestic production meeting the environmental standard.

There were predictions in the US, as well as Germany, of undertaking unilateral changes – that is, changes not agreed across the GATT conferences – if international consensus could not move in this direction. In the richest economies, the new consensus thus was moving rapidly towards imposing duties on imports which did not meet local environmental standards. But the issues remain unresolved, in spite of the 1992 GATT report on these issues.

The impact of environmental legislation

Alongside the rising concern about local environments, people have become increasingly aware that the planetary environment itself is being affected by industrial and urban pollution. For instance, the clearly documented damage to the ozone layer has shown that international action to protect the environment is needed, reflected in the Montreal Agreement of 1989. There is no way of determining whether the expanding ozone gaps over the Antarctic, and recently over the Arctic and Europe, are historically unique or whether for other reasons they have occurred in the past. However, because of the unique threat posed by the potential loss of this layer, causing in essence the disappearance of the Earth's protective shield, global action to reduce the likelihood of loss has become inescapable. The imperative to take action overrides uncertain and incomplete knowledge.

Other environmental issues have similar uncertainty surrounding them. Greenhouse gases – carbon dioxide, nitrogen oxides and so on – have been produced at an accelerating rate over the last 200 years. It is not yet clear to what extent their accumulation in the atmosphere will change the world's environment. Yet in recent years there has been an unprecedented frequency of droughts in East Africa, Western Europe and western North America. Storms have occurred where there were few before. The weight of evidence, while not scientifically irrefutable, is that this pattern of changes might be traced to greenhouse gases and that the production of those gases should be decreased as a matter of prudence.

Pollution does not recognise national boundaries. Thus, the rapid internationalisation of trade and commerce, of investment and production, must be paralleled with the internationalisation of pollution control, energy management and waste management.

The convergent international consensus is that business must take full responsibility for all of its outputs. The increasing requirement for audit and assessment of environmental impacts in the coming decades will affirm in law and regulatory practice the full internalisation of business and government's reprocessing of waste and conservation of energy.

In business, these requirements are likely to spawn further quality controls in such areas as workforce recruitment practices, health and safety, security of employment, opportunities for women and minorities, and product safety. Environmental legislation will extend well-established patterns of management. As companies have done previously with other practices, they will assimilate environmental requirements into their corporate management systems.

Environmental regulations can assist small businesses and competitive dynamics as they fragment traditionally stable product markets and create new opportunities for product innovation. Products must be designed, tested, piloted and marketed in such a way that their potential environmental (and other) liabilities are wholly encompassed. Sometimes small startup companies are quicker to identify niche markets than are large companies.

In some cases large companies have better facilities for product design protection and patenting: where environmental products are involved, this means that it may be easier for small inventors to sell a newly established product line on to a larger concern than to market it themselves.

Small businesses can be assisted by large firms which are increasingly responding to the need for networked business innovation from energetic managers and allowing spin-off firms to be centres of new product development. Environmental legislation can further this trend in some domains: for instance within the EC Agricultural Programme (CAP), small farms, if properly managed, can be made to pay more easily under environmental constraints than large farms. This reflects consumer willingness to pay higher prices for organically grown produce and meat. In other product areas, where craft traditions attract a premium consumer response, green companies also have the possibility of taking a major role.

SUMMARY

This chapter has briefly scanned the emergence of legislation governing the relation between business and the environment, and has shown that it is a worldwide trend. There is widespread agreement within industrial nations and in the developing world that sustainable development requires changes in the way business manages its products, wastes and emissions. In each of the three Triad economies – North America, Europe and Japan/East Asia – environmental sustainability will both impose regulatory constraints and offer business opportunities driving towards corporate product innovation. In many cases this will provide a new range of investment and technological opportunities for the next century, as well as major threats, which no business can afford to ignore.

2 THE GREENING OF CORPORATE STRATEGIES[1]

Issues of corporate management are at the heart of environmental problems. Organisations simultaneously generate wealth and environmental degradation. However, only in the last decade of the 20th century have businesses begun to address the fact that they require a benign and ample physical environment in which to be able to sustain their future activities.

Since the Second World War, the multinational corporation has developed as a global economic force. The Fortune 500 companies are richer, and better able to control their futures, than many of the less developed member states of the United Nations. Therefore, in so far as environmental sustainability is to be reached, it must be in large part through the established capacities of international business. Such businesses are best able to innovate and change direction in response to public pressure, new legislation and new scientific understanding.

The environmental agenda is no longer one of ethical or social sentiment, or of mere do-gooder investment on the part of business. The environmental agenda is now at the heart of corporate strategy. Without a secure base of environmental resources, no business anywhere on the planet is safe from legal, political or financial pressures. The environmental challenge provides a much more formidable and permanent target for business than socialism or communism ever did, because a healthy environment is a necessary prerequisite for a healthy business.

However, if business ever required all its skills at planning and innovation, it is surely in the environmental area. We will never face a more difficult problem than to ensure that our products, factories, processes and distribution systems are not only not damaging to the environment, but in some way or other even enhance it. That is the standard to which our children and grandchildren will hold us.

No matter how imposing the environmental agenda is from a regulatory point of view, it must fight for practical implementation against other business goals, including financial, strategic, operational and political goals. This chapter reviews some recent experience of how companies have begun to grapple with these conflicts.

Figure 2.1 shows John Elkington's dramatic perception of the accelerating number of trading sectors which will be expected to perform to high environmental standards. What is new in this list over that for previous decades is the presence of the large service industries, including insurance, banking and schools. For the first time the 'soft' service sector, much of it the public sector, will be under pressure to improve its environmental performance. The implication is that most organisations will be adopting an environmental programme of some description.

FAST-MOVING CONSUMER GOODS (FMCG)

The most difficult environmental challenges are faced by those companies which, over the last 100 years, have developed a range of goods which are sold in many different countries, sometimes in varying formats. Producers and marketers of such items as groceries, domestic cleaning agents and pre-cooked food for takeaway all form a major component of modern economies, and rely on a range of disposable packaging and products which are dumped into the environment after use.

With the development of 'strict liability', especially in European and North American legal codes, the key elements of these industries will be undergoing fundamental alterations in coming years. For instance, in early 1992 German law required that manufacturers begin to take control of their products' packaging: successive legislation in coming years will require increasing proportions of the packaging to be recycled. This law is liable to be replicated in other OECD countries.

History shows that businesses confronted with such requirements aim typically to convert what has become a liability into an asset. For instance, by the 1960s, sawdust, a by-product of old-fashioned sawmill operations, had been converted into an important component in a new product, hardboard. These secondary products have formed an important additional source of profit for the forest products industry in recent decades.

It is thus probable that companies faced with tighter packaging laws will search for ways to make their containers permanent and of some long-term utility to consumers, especially in the fast-moving consumer groups (FMCG) sector. Disposable containers will be turned into desirable objects. Polluting plastics may well be displaced by more easily

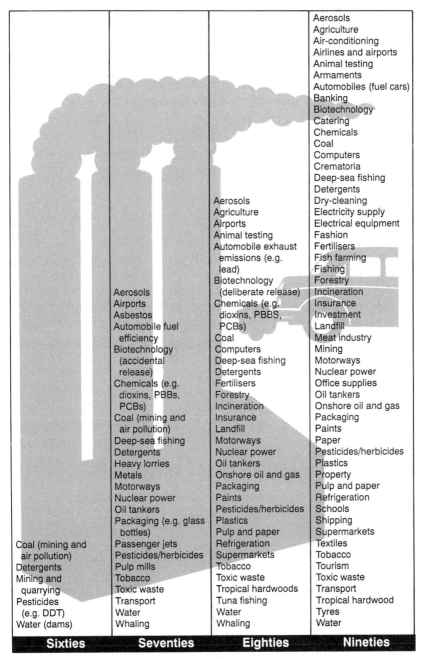

Sixties	Seventies	Eighties	Nineties
Coal (mining and air pollution) Detergents Mining and quarrying Pesticides (e.g. DDT) Water (dams)	Aerosols Airports Asbestos Automobile fuel efficiency Biotechnology (accidental release) Chemicals (e.g. dioxins, PBBs, PCBs) Coal (mining and air pollution) Deep-sea fishing Detergents Heavy lorries Metals Motorways Nuclear power Oil tankers Packaging (e.g. glass bottles) Passenger jets Pesticides/herbicides Pulp mills Tobacco Toxic waste Transport Water Whaling	Aerosols Agriculture Airports Animal testing Automobile exhaust emissions (e.g. lead) Biotechnology (deliberate release) Chemicals (e.g. dioxins, PBBS, PCBs) Coal Computers Deep-sea fishing Detergents Fertilisers Forestry Incineration Insurance Landfill Motorways Nuclear power Oil tankers Onshore oil and gas Packaging Paints Pesticides/herbicides Plastics Pulp and paper Refrigeration Supermarkets Tobacco Toxic waste Tropical hardwoods Tuna fishing Water Whaling	Aerosols Agriculture Air-conditioning Airlines and airports Animal testing Armaments Automobiles (fuel cars) Banking Biotechnology Catering Chemicals Coal Computers Crematoria Deep-sea fishing Detergents Dry-cleaning Electricity supply Electrical equipment Fashion Fertilisers Fish farming Fishing Forestry Incineration Insurance Investment Landfill Meat industry Mining Motorways Nuclear power Office supplies Oil tankers Onshore oil and gas Packaging Paints Paper Pesticides/herbicides Plastics Property Pulp and paper Refrigeration Schools Shipping Supermarkets Textiles Tobacco Tourism Toxic waste Transport Tropical hardwood Tyres Water

Source: J. Elkington, et al. *The Green Business Guide,* 1991

Figure 2.1   Industries in the firing line

recycled glass bottles and jars. Some forms of plastic will be comprehensively recycled as is now becoming standard with petro-ethylene-
tetrachloride (PET) plastic drink bottles for carbonated drinks.

In all these areas, companies working with public authorities for waste
disposal and pollution control will require a period of development and
product redesign. The costs of this will be borne by the normal product
development budgets of the corporate plans. Co-ordination with public
authorities will be vital, as these authorities have the legal powers to veto
or reject plans for product containers that do not conform to the performance standards which are emerging from various legislation.

McDonald's

McDonald's, the giant hamburger chain, is now as much part of the
American global identity as the American flag and Coca-Cola.
McDonald's has penetrated every national economy, lacking outlets
only in such closed societies as Burma, North Korea and some of the
African states. Indeed, the business revolution they pioneered turned
serving cooked food into a fast-moving consumer goods FMCG sector.
Traditionally restaurants and cafés had been decentralised small
businesses.

The international scale of the business is seldom seen: McDonald's'
annual turnover is now estimated at about $21 billion (£12 billion).
Founded as recently as the 1950s, it is already a key component in the
global economy. For instance it raises beef in all countries with outlets,
potatoes in many locations (but always to a single standard) and
generates a demand for plastic and paper packaging which has considerable impact on waste disposal, and production and recycling techniques.

In some countries (e.g. the US) McDonald's operates as a system of
independently owned franchises, whereas in others (e.g. the UK) it
works both as a chain owned by a single company and as franchises. Tax
laws and financial logic have dictated the varying structures of
McDonald's' ownership. Control over the quality and environmental
impact of the output provides a major central feature – the unique selling
proposition (USP) for McDonald's.

The rapid spread of McDonald's and other fast-food chains through
the eastern European bloc has reflected consumers' perceptions of style,
quality and value for money associated with its products. The
McDonald's empire has in many areas set new standards which other
industries have had to learn to emulate in order to survive: they were

among the first to show how low-skilled and low-paid counter staff can work efficiently and with high morale. They showed that sanitation and amenity could be achieved alongside financial success and they are a textbook company for Total Quality Control in their operations.

However, not surprisingly the company's environmental profile is not good. McDonald's were seen to be environmentally damaging in both their food purchases and origins, and their product packaging. There have also been concerns with the nutritional quality of the McDonald's products. But more damaging have been erroneous claims that the company's beef originated from ranches built in the Amazon basin on the ruins of the rain forest. A further concern is that the containers used for the McDonald's products used chloro-fluorocarbons (CFCs), chemicals which are linked to ozone destruction.

These environmentally-based criticisms have presented a challenge to McDonald's' corporate adaptability. Environmental issues have become an additional set of quality targets influencing the company's management procedures. The company's response has been to undertake a comprehensive environmental audit of both its processes and its products. The results of the audit have so far not been made public: however, an initial target, publicly announced, has been to replace CFC-based packaging wholly with non-polluting substitutes by 1993. The result of this audit may well lead to the development of a far-reaching environmental strategy which will systematically identify and target for change all of the company's operations which cause environmental damage.

The key issue is how to retain profitability at all points of the value chain. McDonald's' USP is its principal attraction in gaining continued customer loyalty and repeat purchase: a standardised product instantly available at a competitive price, consumable on or off the premises. McDonald's as a business concept has succeeded because customers have been willing to pay for all elements of the product, including the excessive packaging, large shipping distances and remote sourcing of raw materials. The challenge will be how to retain this USP if, as a result of a future environmental programme, the product becomes either more expensive or less convenient.

If McDonald's can devise an environmentally friendly approach which retains the profitability of the business, then it is conceivable that all FMCG sectors, including the 10,000 or more items on supermarket shelves around the world, can also be redirected into becoming strategic environmental businesses. Thus, the environmental agenda presents one of the most successful of American rapid-growth businesses with a major challenge. The use of meat-based products served in throwaway containers, a brilliant innovation of the 1950s, may by the turn of the century have become both too expensive and unpopular. Can McDonald's devise vegetable-based products packaged in recyclable containers, which have the same popularity as Big Macs? The prediction is that it is likely to be able to do just that.

Reckitt and Colman

Some of the governing principles in designing products that can qualify for the new green labelling laws and codes are becoming apparent. First, the origin of their materials must be certified as environmentally benign: endangered species may not be used, nor may industrial processes used in the materials' production generate unacceptable levels or forms of pollution, e.g. CFCs. Secondly, the use of the product itself must be environmentally neutral. For example, the use of cleansing materials is increasingly moving away from environmentally toxic chemicals like bleach, and Reckitt and Colman's toilet cleansers are an example of this.

In the UK and British Commonwealth, Reckitt and Colman is one of the oldest household products' names, whose products range from table mustard (many varieties) to toilet cleansers. In 1991 Reckitt and Colman introduced a new range of cleansing products to the marketplace. Based on consumer research, sea lions, dolphins and whales were used to key the new 'Down to Earth' product range of cleaners.

Until the arrival of the environmental agenda, household cleaners were a slow-growth and stable product area with large producers dominating the market in each country. With the new environmental awareness consumers began to try out the interlopers into this settled marketplace. But there was disappointment as these products turned out to contain not altogether benign elements (e.g. bleach) and not to work as well as the established market leaders, in the UK Harpic, Dettol and Brasso. Substantial product development was required by Reckitt and Colman to produce replacements which, while environmentally friendly, were also marketable within the traditional marketplace.

Consumers clearly do not want to move from known producers they have trusted for years. But the known producer must make a genuine effort to ensure the continuing use of their product by increasingly sophisticated and demanding consumers. This is done by innovative product lines which reflect not only the new technology but also the new consumer requirement of technological benignness. In this case, the new products work as well as the traditional products, cost the same and are environmentally more benign (see *Financial Times* Knight, 1991).

INDUSTRIAL SUPPLY INDUSTRIES

Major chemical and petrochemical companies provide one of the bedrock structures in the modern global economy. Their major customers tend to be other technologically-advanced companies who use their products in the manufacture of a final range of consumer products. Many very large companies are almost unknown to the general public, in that they mainly advertise to their customers in industry. Because they often use potentially harmful and complex industrial processes, which they also wish to keep secret from their competitors, they take great precautions to avoid environmental disasters, either through chronic low-level pollution of their surroundings or through catastrophic mistakes in plant management.

The nuclear industry is the most dramatic of these industries. In the early days of nuclear power, it was hoped that its environmental impacts would be very low. After all, nuclear power generation came into being alongside the infamously polluting brown coal power plants of a previous generation, which generated excessive local pollution (by sulphur and other dioxides), as well as the outputs which produced acid rain sometimes hundreds of miles downwind.

Unhappily, the leakage of radiation from civilian nuclear installations has turned out to be more insidious than the first generation of plant designers realised. It would appear from research in the 1980s that microscopic levels of contamination can influence the genetic patterns of plant workers and predispose some of their children to above-average numbers of cases of leukaemia. The cumulative emissions of very low-level radioactivity have also apparently polluted beaches along the Irish Sea coast in north-west England.

The recently-developed guidelines under the international standards of Control of Substances Hazardous to Health (COSHH) are requiring ever more rigorous procedures, particularly where hazardous chemicals are in use. For the purposes of corporate governance and shareholder interest, however, strategic guidance of these industries must take on sharper and more detailed control over potential environmental impacts, be they hazardous or low level. The trend towards increasing major legal claims by both governments and communities against businesses responsible for health risks arising from plant operations demands energetic testing of all installations for possible risks.

Union Carbide

The case of Union Carbide and its partly-owned subsidiary in Bhopal, India highlights many of the difficulties involved in the control of complex industrial biochemical industries. The giant chemical firm Union Carbide was one of the earliest American companies to expand its business interests into the developing world. Their first Indian business was founded in the early decades of the 20th century.

Local management, particularly that in countries other than that of the founding parent, has a built-in desire to establish local autonomy. National governments wish to retain increasing proportions of skill and investment after the initial returns on the technology transfer and industrial investment have been established. However, local skills may fall short through lack of sustained contact with best practice available internationally.

In the 1960s the Indian government required that holdings of overseas firms should become at least half Indian in ownership. Responding to Indian law, Union Carbide committed itself to a lengthy programme of local ownership and control, while retaining a developmental and quality responsibility for the business. Its share of profits was reinvested within India. By the 1980s all non-Indian operatives and managers at the plant had been replaced by Indian staff.

At that time the pesticide Sevin was being manufactured in the largest plant of its kind in India by Union Carbide India Limited, the Indian-controlled subsidiary of the American parent. Until the 1970s the pesticide was generated from non-toxic chemicals, imported and combined into the final product on site. There were minimal toxic dangers involved in the process. The final product is mildly toxic. The Indianisation of the plant brought with it the requirement that 'upstream' activities of chemical manufacture should occur within India, to retain more of the economic activity within the country. This meant that highly toxic chemicals, especially methyl isocyanate (MIC), would be stored on-site and transmitted from there.

MIC had been manufactured as a product for some years. It is highly toxic and Indian staff were intensively trained in its management. Outside the 80-acre (34 hectares) factory in Bhopal a shanty town had been allowed to grow up, made up of some 40,000 indigent rural migrants able to make a marginal living off the local activity engendered by the pesticide factory.

On the night of 2 December 1984, engineers noticed increased pressure in one of the holding tanks. However, as this was not abnormal, they took their midnight break. By the time they returned, the pressure had increased and an explosive release of MIC was saturating the plant and the downwind shanty town with toxic fumes. By dawn some 4,000 people were dead and dying in and near the plant, and 300 yards away in the railway town of Bhopal.

Although in theory the Bhopal explosion was at one remove from the American parent whose share was only 49 per cent, the top management layer of Union Carbide was quick to take full responsibility for the deaths and the 100,000 injuries which occurred. The Indian government was also keenly aware that damage settlements in American courts would be far higher than in Indian courts.

The key issue for the parent company has been to arrive at a better understanding about how to exercise appropriate control in a partly-owned foreign subsidiary without abrogating local management's responsibilities and sense of control. Since the Bhopal disaster, new protocols and controls have become established throughout the international biochemical industry (Sharplin, 1989).

DIVERSIFYING MULTINATIONALS

Dow Chemical

A number of leading international corporations have anticipated the continuing advances of environmental legislation. Dow Chemical, an American-based company with a diversified product range, from household food plastic wraps to napalm for bombs, suffered severe damage to its public reputation as a responsible industrialist during the 1960s. Responding to the threat of continued social, political and legal action against its products, Dow decided during the late 1970s to review all of the company's products and plant over a 10-year development period. By the late 1980s, Dow's product portfolio and plant standards had in large part become accepted as an international best standard. Dow's management has been repeatedly acknowledged as a model for the chemical industry's environmental efforts worldwide.

Norsk Hydro

Some European companies have been involved for years in reinvesting to enhance their environmental performance. Norsk Hydro, the largest Norwegian industrial concern, is one example. The company is a major producer of oil, gas and hydro-electricity, and its downstream products include petrochemicals and plastics. Its fertiliser operations have also expanded rapidly, to the point that Norsk is now the biggest supplier of fertilisers in the world. Salmon farming and fishfood products are recent diversifications. Other Norsk Hydro industries include aluminium and magnesium extraction, and the manufacture of biomarine and biomedical products.

Through acquisition and merger, Norsk Hydro's largest market and centre of production is in the UK, where it has 2,000 employees and a turnover of £400 million, compared to its worldwide turnover of £800 million (about $1.5 billion).

Like many Scandinavian companies, Norsk Hydro has grown since the 1950s within a climate of corporate social responsibility. Thus, when it reviewed its global activities in 1990, it took a public view of both the strengths and the shortcomings of its environmental performance. Norsk Hydro's environmental review covered products and technology in 60 countries.

Because of the complex production processes which form the core of the company's manufacturing processes, it has been the company's consistent aim to use all of the by-products of its manufacturing systems as feedstock for other products. Typically its 20 production sites are self-sufficient in energy, recycling both energy and chemical after-products. Most of its plants have been modernised in recent years, with a major target of reducing both liquid and air-borne emissions.

A typical plant is the Immingham factory in the Humber estuary, in north-east England. One of many major industrial developers in the area, Norsk has for many years maintained an environmental liaison committee with local communities and councils. This committee's members include local councillors, environmental health officers, government pollution inspectors and site managers from the company. At six-month intervals, it reviews company operations on-site, looking in detail at gaseous and liquid discharge levels and at environmental complaints. Complaints coming in are dealt with immediately by on-site staff chemists and managers.

Among the environmental performance programmes being implemented in 1991 were the following:

- use of mission statements covering behaviour towards the environment in all production companies;
- regular environmental reports on all sites, including both monthly site management reports and quarterly business unit reports;
- attainment of high standards on vinyl chloride monomer and dust from the PVC plant;
- attainment of effluent treatment standards, which in some cases include biological cleansing processes;
- the production of animal food and fish oil from the wastes of food plants;
- well-organised complaint-handling procedures at all sites; and
- strong involvement at all sites with affected local communities and councils. (Norsk Hydro, 1991)

ICI

Other major companies have been slower to anticipate the advance of environmental legislation. Britain's ICI produces a wide variety of chemical-based products, including paints, fertilisers and a range of industrial chemicals. One of the top twenty companies in Europe, it continues to improve environmental standards for both its plant and its products, as EC legislation tightens on the chemical industry. Like many other European companies, it is implementing a long-term investment programme to ensure that the environmental performance of its plant and products will attain appropriate standards early in the new century. In spite of this programme, however, accusations of commercial pragmatism have appeared: even as the UK signed the Montreal Protocol of 1989 agreeing to ban production of halons (a group of ozone-depleting chemicals), ICI products based on halons were reportedly being marketed in countries like Pakistan and Chile which had not signed the Protocol (Ryan and Palmer, 1991).

CAPITAL GOODS

Buildings and cars form the two largest areas of consumer and business purchase.[2] They each involve the use of many production processes and hundreds of different materials. They bring together all the industries which lie at the core of modern economies, ranging from advanced electronics to the building and handcrafts involved in their final assembly. For this reason, the evolution of 'green' standards for these two product areas forms one of the major governmental and industrial challenges in the coming decades. If these two areas' environmental impacts can be substantially reduced or made benign, then the problems of other industries will be largely manageable.

Buildings and cars have become more energy efficient over time. This process has occurred not just in recent years, but since their modern forms were first adopted in the early decades of the 20th century. With the potential threats of global warming and resource shortages, however, the emphasis on developing low-impact personal transport and habitat technologies is intensifying.

The biohouse

Buildings comprise the largest long-term capital goods in the human environment. The evolution of new materials during the last century has fundamentally altered human expectations about both the performance and the appearance of housing and workplaces. Essentially, affluent societies expect that internal temperatures will be maintained within a few degrees of 20° C, whether in cold or hot conditions. For the service-based office work which has dominated recent decades, much of the planet requires air conditioning during the hot seasons, and in many cases throughout the year. The enormous increase in economic activity in tropical regions, including the southern USA, is largely due to air conditioning in home, office, factory and car.

Green pressure groups have been articulate in suggesting that human societies should return to traditional methods of controlling body comfort, in other words, through adjustments in clothing, as well as through the use of the siesta in hot climates. Traditional building methods, especially in the southern and eastern Mediterranean and in Islamic societies, have used many sophisticated low-technology methods of generating air movements during hot seasons. The Arabic souk, the traditional robes of the desert Arab, and the courtyards and fountains of palace and city were all successful in lowering temperatures without imposing excessive energy requirements or using energy-intensive technology.

In temperate environments with moderate seasonality – most of Europe, northern North America, Japan – air conditioning requirements can be reduced by up to three-quarters with high levels of insulation, correct window placement, reduction of window area and proper use of solar power.

Building materials can often be derived from recycled waste products. The international glut of car tyres, a source of much industrial recycling research, has produced a number of cheap, high-performance building materials which may become commercially and architecturally viable over coming years.

However, the search for biobuildings has focused most of all on energy conservation and the use of passive solar energy, now a maturing development with established technologies. The use of renewable energy sources, greater mechanical efficiency in power transmission and production, and the increased deployment of high-quality insulation techniques are all having major impacts on energy consumption. Building technology responds rather than leads in the search for energy conservation.

An example of the use of 'green' building materials can be found in the Greenpeace headquarters in London. The architects, Feilden Clegg Design, used the following materials.

Windows	standardised
	energy conserving; links to passive solar collection system
	positioned and sized to maximise desirable solar gain and
	minimise undesirable solar gain
Insulation	oil, mineral or cellulose-based
Paints	solvent-based; organic-based
Floor coverings	vinyl; polypropylene; linoleum; sisal; wool
Internal fittings	aluminium; wood (but preservative problem)

(*Environment Guardian*, November 1991).

The zero-impact car

The best-known legislation controlling the environmental impacts of cars is that of Southern California. The region is permeated by cars. Although there have been many advances in mass public transit, including the construction of the Greater Los Angeles subway system, cars still form the core of personal transport and indeed the culture. Due to its geography, Los Angeles also suffers from chronic pollution due to stagnant air caught in temperature inversion domes. In some cases severe restrictions on car movements are required during these periods, and in 1992 a system of tradeable pollution permits was instituted.

In 1990, with the backing of state regulations, local councils in the

Greater Los Angeles region adopted statutory targets for car companies. By the year 2000 car companies in the area must sell at least 10 per cent of their new cars as 'zero-emission vehicles', otherwise their other products will be banned from sale.

Recognising that this is the beginning of an international trend, many car manufacturers have research underway aimed in the end at production of zero-emission vehicles. By the mid 1990s, it is projected that car manufacturers will have transformed their products into low-emission, 100 per cent recyclable machines. If such new technologies are not undertaken, it is conceivable that the car industry, the largest manufacturing sector on the planet, will be environmentally obsolete by the second quarter of the 21st century.

THE DEVELOPMENT/PLANNING SECTOR

Large-scale property development projects can be planned from ecological priorities. Two recent examples of published plans in the south of England exemplify this approach. The first, in East Kent, is rural; the second is in the centre of London.

East Kent International Business Campus

The International Business Campus is designed for state-of-the-art international businesses and local enterprises in the technological and service industries. The site will include ecological design features which will assist both in marketing and in gaining development consents. By the time of its occupancy in the late 1990s, it will form the most advanced 'ecobusiness park' in the UK.

The site of 52 acres (21 hectares) is positioned on a hilltop with dramatic views of the English Channel across the town of Deal. The nearest residential area is about ¼ mile to the east of the site. The site itself is on stable chalk with infilled extraction pits whose main workings are 1 mile distant. A prolonged period of mineral working has left the site with little surface vegetation and generally sterile surface soils.

Present proposals for development include 360,000 feet^2 of office-industrial space and 200,000 feet^2 of housing on 52 acres, totalling 560,000 feet^2 of built space. The proposed architectural approach will be in keeping with local Kent building styles. The built area, including car parks, will cover about 60 per cent of the surface area of the site.

Key features of the proposed development are:

- 12 major high-technology office units for international businesses and technology corporations;
- energy conservation and recycling;
- waste recycling and management;
- wildlife conservation and enhancement;
- local community enterprise accommodation;
- a university-backed international export marketing training and development centre; and
- 150 housing units, with attached studio workspaces.

There will be frequent water features linked to on-site water treatment and recycling systems. The site will be intensively landscaped for wind-sheltering and amenity. Use of wind turbines linked to gas turbines, alongside waste-burning in a combined heat and power-generating station is projected, with potential sales into the national electricity grid. Buildings will be constructed using the highest standards of energy conservation and green materials available, based on leading Anglo-Dutch-German research and trials at Energy Park, Milton Keynes.

It is projected that the business campus will create up to 1,200 jobs, compared with the 1,000 jobs offered in the mid 1960s by coal-mining activities. Recent projections for Dover and the surrounding district suggest the loss of up to 9,000 jobs during the mid 1990s, as a consequence of the EuroTunnel and other changes. No other local site capable of creating 1,000 jobs will be available until the end of the decade.

Access to European infrastructure is good: the driving time to Folkestone's International Euroterminal will be 25 minutes in 1997, on the basis of presently programmed highway improvements. Air service to Europe is provided at Manston International Airport in Ramsgate, 15 minutes' driving time away.

The profile of end-user owner/leasers will concentrate on international trading and technology corporations (European, Japanese, American), local enterprises supplying this sector and the local economy, and north-west European markets. Project marketing will allow units and leases to be pre-sold prior to site acquisition. Tests for marketability, yield and rental levels are positive and built into the business plan.

The project creates an opportunity for a leading property group to take a forward position in the UK EuroRegion location. These locations are expected to show gains over the next decade which, on the basis of present market trends, will be attractive compared to those of other UK locations.

King's Cross Railway Lands

A major new urban quarter is planned for the King's Cross London Railway Land which encompasses 138 acres (55 hectares) at the northern edge of London's central area. This presently under-used and run-down urban area is to be regenerated over a 15-year period into a new high-quality urban quarter with substantial elements of social housing. Its design will from the first involve extensive local resident participation in the form of 'Planning for Real' community forums and citizen participation exercises.

Key elements of the proposed development areas follows.

- Two thousand seven hundred units of social and middle-income housing, largely in housing association tenancies, which are expected to house about 7,000 persons by the year 2002.
- A financially viable proportion of commercial, hotel and retail space near the EuroTunnel rail terminal and its immediate environs to the north.
- A total built area of 3 million feet^2 (alternative proposals have indicated up to 11 million feet^2) to be built between 1992 and 2002.
- A build-out construction value of £1.5 billion.
- A system of green building standards affecting all buildings and urban spaces, to make them energy-efficient, secure and long-lasting. This is to be implemented through a green design guide, to be established by the developers and local councils.
- A design requirement on all construction to be built to highest international standards.
- A range of community facilities, training and holistic health centres, employment centres, shops and light industry.
- Regeneration of the Regent's Canal as a major urban greenway and focus of leisure, recreational and limited commercial development. This will provide shops, restaurants, cafés, boat basins and walkways.
- An ecological and wildlife support system and landscaping throughout the site. The expansion of the Camley Street Nature Park will provide a wildlife reserve for Inner London communities.
- Emphasis on pedestrian and bicycle access, restriction of through traffic, and comprehensive neighbourhood safety and security systems.

- Retention and reuse of all listed buildings and many unlisted older buildings. This will expand the conservation and heritage environments in the King's Cross and Regent's Canal Conservation Areas across the whole of the site.
- A new International Centre for Metropolitan Ecology, with the aim of transferring skills, ideas and exchanges with a developing country metropolis, in this case Bombay, India. The centre has the express purpose of transferring technology of urban management to India as required by the dynamics of Bombay's own development. This is the first proposed case of metropolitan twinning.

British Rail are to build a major rail terminal at the southern end of the site, to receive EuroTunnel rail traffic from the late 1990s. It proposes to retain the Grade II listed Great Northern Hotel and to integrate this structure into the new concourse which will link the existing Grade I listed stations of St Pancras and King's Cross. This proposed development will be entirely insulated from the railway tunnels beneath the site, which will be engineered throughout to keep dust, noise, vibration and other railway operational impacts away from the development area.

The key policies for the development were:

- to balance the needs and aspirations of the local community with those of London and the wider region;
- to produce realistic and financially viable investment proposals, linked to market projections for the 1990s;
- to design a 'Green' community development strategy suitable for the London of the 21st century.

The proposal was designed over 18 months, during 1989–90. The planning exercises benefited from the formal and informal advice of such groups as:

- higher education institutions;
- King's Cross residents and community groups, including hundreds of local residents;
- local primary and secondary schools;
- local councillors from the London Boroughs of Camden and Islington; and
- about 25 leading environmental planners, architects, surveyors, and other London-based experts in large project development and community participation procedures.

The exercise and consequent proposal reflect the philosophies and methods that will be required for urban planning, architectural design and the property industry for the new century. The recession of the 1990s reduces the likelihood of this and competing proposals proceeding at King's Cross until the new century.

Notes

1 Malcolm Hutton advised on the development of this chapter.
2 Changes in car and building design have been detailed in the following newspaper and journal articles on which this section relies:
Beavis, Simon, 'Plug in to the mid-green car', *Guardian*, 6 September 1991.
Daniels, Jeff, 'California sets exhausting standards'. *Financial Times*, 11 September 1991.
Yates, Andrew, 'The ideal home turns a dark shade of green', *Sunday Times*, 17 March 1991.

3 TRENDS IN CORPORATE STRATEGY AND ENVIRONMENTAL ISSUES

Chapter 2 indicated some of the environmental initiatives presently under-way in the international business setting. Chapter 3 considers corporate strategy from the environmental perspective.

THE IMPACT OF ENVIRONMENTAL ISSUES ON TRANSNATIONAL CORPORATE STRATEGY

The discipline of corporate strategic planning and management for large firms has evolved over the last half century (e.g. see Chandler, 1939; Vernon, 1971; Porter, 1980, 1985, 1990; Vernon-Wortzel and Wortzel, 1991). This chapter focuses on a number of concepts in corporate strategy and shows how they are being altered by the environmental agenda. The aim is to assist the manager involved with environmental audit to begin to consider how strategic decisions may be affected by the environmental responsibilities of the corporation.

Elements of corporate strategy affect the pace and scope of environmental audit: these, too, must be brought into environmental strategy. The interplay of corporate strategy and environmental responsibility has only recently begun to be considered. Corporate strategy will inevitably be affected by the complex environmental agenda emerging internationally, and within national and regional markets. Investor preferences will alter in response to the changing regulatory landscape. In this discussion, there are no final answers. The manager must continue to learn and integrate new environmental concerns into corporate strategy. The intention is to suggest how he or she might, using imagination, consider the strategic implications of rapidly accumulating environmental pressures on his or her organisation.

Companies have been expanding beyond national borders for

hundreds of years. Generally their strategic concerns have been financial and operational, for instance whether they can produce a better return on capital by overseas investment rather than by home expansion. In recent years this has been particularly true in Europe and Japan as the corporate sector has invested aggressively in North American and Asian markets.

These Triad economies – North America, Europe and Japan/East Asia – comprise over 65 per cent of the planetary economy with less than 20 per cent of the population (Ohmae, 1985). Each of the Triad economic communities is developing increasingly demanding environmental regulations. Companies are responding accordingly, seeing in environmental issues areas of business development and competitive advantage. To function effectively among the Triad economies, a company will have to be seen to be keeping up with its competitors in environmental issues.

International strategists see environmental concerns as increasingly governing the acceptability of both products and plant. The multinational corporation must be able to assimilate and proactively interact with local environmental law and consumer preference in order to continue to be able to survive and flourish in a multiplicity of market settings.

Environmental audit as a major new element in corporate strategy will affect many of the key strategic decisions concerning transnational and multinational companies.[1] Opportunities and problems of strategic investment are not always high on the agenda of the environmental manager involved in establishing the corporate environmental programme. However, as integrated pollution control (IPC) and other environmental regulation, as well as investor and consumer preference, affect share values and stock markets, increasingly strategic investment will be examined for its environmental impacts.

Indeed, business entrepreneurs across all the service sector have been quick to spot these trends. For instance, by the early 1990s every large accountancy and legal firm in America and Europe had environmental law and environmental impact groups, many of them multi-disciplinary. This capacity allows them to advise corporate clients on environmental ramifications of new investment and divestment. It will become increasingly cost-effective to build such expertise into the corporate management structure of large companies, rather than paying for it through consultancy relationships.

COMPETITIVE ADVANTAGE IN THE CORPORATE ENVIRONMENTAL REVOLUTION: THE MULTINATIONAL SECTOR

Sectoral balance (vertical integration) versus service-sector (end-consumer) expansion

Recent decades suggest that higher profits can be gained from concentrating on endpoints of value in the value chain: for instance Marks and Spencer, the leading British clothing retailer, has produced continuous profit growth as a retailer, not in manufacturing. The oil multinationals have expanded 'downstream' through more gasoline/petrol service stations. With the world surplus of oil and falling prices during the 1980s, oil extraction has not been a stable source of profits growth, whereas the retail trade has offered expansion opportunities through diversification of retail outlets. This has meant that horizontal investment at the consumer level has been more rewarding.

Integrated pollution control requires that environmental impacts – e.g. product health impacts, site pollution at production plants – will have to be controlled by producers. Additional skills and value-added inputs will therefore be required during primary production. This will increase management costs and attract higher-skill managers. This trend suggests that major margin increases at the producer level may increase the profit potential for primary producers.

Multinational vertical integration will be increasingly attractive. The economies of IPC, from initial extraction to final consumption, will increasingly be captured through product strategies which integrate each level of production and distribution.

Technology leadership versus marketing leadership

Market-led companies have had a high growth dynamic for some decades. With the coming environmental revolution, the development of environmental technology may provide additional elements of competitive advantage for technology-intensive companies. This means, of course, that the nature of their marketing expertise must now encompass environmental considerations. Indeed, it suggests that the technology of process management and of recycling must be seen as part of the product technology. Improvements in such areas are highly valued by consumers and can be used in determining final prices: consumers will tolerate some degree of price increase for products with 'green' credentials.

The car industry is a case in point. Rather than being seen as a product in the normal limited sense, the car has become reinterpreted as a major environmental process. The consumer's buying decision is only one of a number of steps involved in transportation (personal, private, point to point). But society increasingly views the car as a production element: it begins with resource and energy extraction, and ends in a product whose recycled elements are reinvested in the production cycle or returned to the ground in a non-polluting form, able to be restructured into further product cycles in the future.

Increasingly, the industry speaks not only of zero-emission vehicles but of zero-impact vehicles, cars which are made, perform and then disappear, leaving nil impact on the environment. This is a visionary view of the most polluting of all current technologies, if only because of its universality and universal desirability. It aims at no less than long-term sustainability for the car industry. Without zero-impact vehicles, it would be inconceivable to equip such societies as China and India with cars, which represent over one-third of the human population of almost six billion. Yet these countries have economic growth rates and aspirations which may in the end bring about similar levels of car ownership as those of, say, The Netherlands or the UK, where there is about one car for every two persons.

In the early 1990s, German and Japanese transnational companies, with worldwide production and sales in areas like cars and electronics, were also the leading ecological developers. Volkswagen, Toshiba, Mercedes Benz, and Nissan all were working towards zero-impact process and product technosystems.

Similarly, the built environment, including buildings, railways, roads and the whole of the supporting infrastructure, is increasingly viewed as a technology whose impacts must be neutralised or indeed made environmentally positive. Corporations able to develop and build such technological systems will have major marketing advantages during the next half century.

Porter and others have pointed consistently towards the challenges that international companies face in developing competitive advantages that arise naturally from their own background. A company with a long record of social responsibility in its strategy and operations, such as IBM or Apple Corporation, will find that its culture will adopt a more beneficial legal and marketing approach towards the environment, with only minor modifications. Companies with traditions in such areas as worker co-management structures and employee profit participation, such as many of those found in Germany and Japan, will also move naturally into an environmental mode. Volvo, the Swedish car manufacturer, for example, sees its environmental strategy as a simple extension of its many decades of safety and worker-sharing approach.

Private sector investment versus public/private sector investment strategies

Multi-sectoral investment economies – that is, economies where government agencies work actively and visibly with private companies in new business areas – grow more quickly, as is evident from the rapid post-war growth rates of Japan, Germany and France. The USA, with much smaller proportions of growth arising from public sector participation in joint ventures, has seen slower growth, except in the defence industry, where joint ventures have dominated with non-defence goods losing out. In the UK in the early 1970s, developing public sector investments were badly crippled by the rise in oil prices. However, North Sea oil, a jointly led investment, was greatly successful and British Airways became successful initially as a state corporation.

The point remains: environmental strategies will arise more spontaneously – and credibly – in investment settings with a long tradition of cross-sectoral investment, because these settings have the most experience of handling a wide array of investment targets, going beyond the financial. By contrast, mining giants like RTZ have only rarely taken community issues on board in their resource extraction policies as a transnational corporation. Many of the large construction and extraction companies, including Bechtel, the American construction giant, may find it difficult to compete with Japanese construction innovators. The Japanese builders claim to be able to safeguard surroundings from all environmental impacts during construction.

Centralisation versus decentralisation

Traditions of local decentralisation for transnational companies, where the companies retain only key controls over financial matters, may be shifting over the next decades to greater decentralisation, where substantial control is left with local management who must respond to a panoply of new regulatory and consumer expectation in each of the national economies. For instance, the new German packaging laws of 1991, which will require comprehensive recycling of all packaging materials used in consumer goods, was, at the time of writing, being described to the EC as an anti-competition practice effectively excluding non-German goods from competing in German markets. GATT was also being appealed to by many, especially American, firms to declare anti-competitive various environmental regulations coming into being in Japan and Germany.

The tendency internationally is to raise all practices to those of the richest countries. This clearly has significance for less well-off economies whose goods must compete overseas against competitors who are better capitalised to handle the new investment required by regulation. Consumers from rich countries are also able to pay the additional cost for full recycling, although some analysts suggest that over time recycling will be self-financing.

The new recycling requirements have generated major new investment challenges for large providers of packaging technologies like Tetrapak, the Anglo-Swedish aluminium and paper container maker; TI, the major European can maker; and for the makers of petro-ethylene-tetrachloride (PET), the soft plastic in which soft drinks are dominantly packaged across the planet.

It is not yet clear whether greater adherence to local environmental regulations will lessen multinational corporations' capacity to transmit their 'innovation culture' from home countries into new markets. Certainly some product sectors are becoming more globalised – Levi's jeans, Nike running shoes, Coca-Cola, IBM, New Kids on the Block, Japanese cars, McDonald's hamburgers and others are becoming more localised – middle-class restaurants, hotels, paper products, business stationery. As it opens in a greater diversity of cultural environments, MacDonalds has found it useful to introduce localised product ranges alongside the flagship international menu, and Benetton, an international Italian clothing company, explicitly individualises its national shops, retaining a common brand image among a diversity of clothing styles in various countries. Thus the transplant of special innovative characteristics of a company or national business culture increasingly requires a capacity to respond to local concerns, many of which will become environmentally programmed.

Scientifically led R & D versus market-led R & D

Increasingly the trend in product research and development has been towards market-triggered products, which have been the source of much Japanese exporting success. With the new emphasis on environmental conservation and low-impact products and processes, the role of product scientists and process engineers will be expanded. The overall amount of research going into product and plant will increase. Inevitably this will mean that firms able to commit additional resources to technological inputs will gain a degree of market advantage: they will be able to bear early product development costs that firms without such skills may find expensive to buy in the open marketplace.

Environmental control and product technology therefore provides multiple new product opportunities. Where consumer satiation in the Triad economies had begun to make product areas less capable of high growth, there will be a period of product replacement in favour of environmentally friendly offerings. Thus, the car industry will experience a period of vehicle replacement that is more rapid than it might otherwise be, as consumers and regulators drive jointly towards higher emission standards and lower environmental impact.

Effective global strategy and innovative capacity of national culture

Analysing competitive advantage among nations, Porter (1990) focuses in particular on the capacity of firms to transplant their innovative corporate cultures into non-home-base cultures. During the second half of the century, American firms have proven their capacity to carry out such transplants in many sectors. In the last 10 years, Japanese firms have begun to carry out an even more aggressive transplant operation, both in North America and Europe.

The environmental agenda promises many challenges to the cultural transplant process. Local regulations will vary considerably among different countries. A product which is profitable in one less intensely regulated national environment may prove unprofitable in a more regulated setting. Importing companies may find the cultural setting too demanding, no matter how deeply seated their innovative cultural characteristics. Greater adherence to non-home-base environmental regulations may make it unprofitable to export: the option would then be subject to franchise or licensing arrangements with the overseas market. This would then lead more naturally to a looser form of marketing alliance than the typical transnational firm represents: a multi-domestic marketing network.

COMPETITIVE ADVANTAGE IN THE CORPORATE ENVIRONMENTAL REVOLUTION

Ethical investment and profits

Alongside strategic considerations internal to the organisation, there are external groups – investors, customers and affected communities – all of whom are stakeholders in the organisation. Increasingly they will be looking to the environmental agenda of the corporation with a number of questions in mind.

'Is the company in compliance with the most recent applicable environmental laws?'

This question is the very minimal ethical standard and indeed reflects more a question of corporate legal commitment that a fundamental ethical stance. External conformity with environmental laws must be sustained even where an internal cultural setting tolerates substantial deviation from the highest environmental (or financial, or social) goals. Thus, for the investor, to have evidence of a compliance audit and of the remedying of any faults discovered during such an audit is on the same plane as evidence of proper standards of financial housekeeping. It is a minimal expectation which should be fulfilled before the corporation is considered for further investment.

'Are the company's products or plants subject to liability for pollution, public safety or other long-term indemnity which will reduce the value for shareholders?'

The question of long-term potential liabilities is less easy to establish by the potential investor. Many court decisions in North America have judged in favour of persons damaged by a company's products or plant, even though the environmental or product liability regulations may have been considerably laxer at the time when the difficulty or injury took place. Liability has been found even where explicit regulation has been lacking, because companies had failed to fulfil the provisions of due care under civil law.

Therefore, the investor must look deeper within corporate strategy to determine whether the company is fully aware of its long-term obligations, some of which may not be presently fixed in legislation or which may arise from court precedents yet to be announced. This is an issue at the heart of corporate ethical culture. A checklist for environmental strategies is given at the end of this chapter.

'Is the company's corporate culture fully committed to the ethical ramifications of environmental optimisation and sustainability?'
The issue of sustainability is at the heart of any company's culture in the form of financial sustainability. Now, the physical environmental setting in which the company functions is increasingly coming to the forefront. A company like Body Shop, with its deep green commitment to products, processes and consumer education, will no doubt be the first of many businesses successfully to adopt the environmental agenda, not just as an additional strategic framework but as the definitive framework for all of its actions, products and communications.

'Has the company's strategic planning taken on board the long-term cultural and technological consequences of environmental issues?'
Finally, the investor must ask whether, after building environmental issues deeply into the strategic core of its development process, the company has undertaken further changes in its processes. This issue was addressed by the president of a large Japanese transnational company: on being asked in a press conference about the company's long-range plans, he replied, 'Well, we have our medium-term 20-year plan but our broad corporate mission is targeted at the middle of the 22nd century.'

The environmental agenda will come to permeate the whole of business culture in the new century and only a determined commitment to its intrinsic values will allow present companies to continue to prosper.

The insurance and reinsurance industries

There is little uniformity between European states with regard to environmental liability insurance. Whereas the UK, for instance, had no general model of good practice in this area as late as 1991, insurers in France, Italy and The Netherlands had developed risk pooling arrangements to cover major industrial and business concerns. This has also been the case in North America. Maritime insurers have, for some decades, agreed insurance coverage and liability for such problems as oil spillage on the high seas.

In many cases government involvement in the reinsurance areas of environmental damage appears to be inevitable. In the 1980s, liability rulings by American courts against UK-based insurers at Lloyd's of

London for long-term asbestosis-linked illnesses sent a shock wave through the reinsurance industry. Claims began to be settled for remote causes which were unprecedented in their extent and distance in time. As a consequence, there is considerable doubt within the insurance industry that private risk underwriting will provide adequate coverage or 'capacity'.

Confronting the range and size of environmental risks which now appear to be legitimately attached to originators of pollution will require new reinsurance mechanisms. In such conditions, a spread of these risks into public funding through general taxation, as is already the case in basic pension provision and social security, may become attractive in many industrialised countries.

TWELVE PRINCIPLES FOR INTEGRATING ENVIRONMENTAL AUDIT INTO CORPORATE STRATEGY

The newly-appointed environmental manager needs to become well placed to carry out initial steps in incorporating corporate environmental programmes into mainstream corporate management. This section proposes 12 principles for integrating an environmental programme into the corporate strategy, which are summarised for reference in Figure 3.1, and will be discussed at greater length in Parts II and III. In this chapter a brief discussion of each principle and its application in an organisational setting follows.

Principle 1   Focus on the corporate learning curve

Environmental goals need to be acquired and assimilated alongside financial, operational and personnel goals. Large organisations are like large ships: to alter their main direction, considerable lead time is necessary. The steering in the new direction must be consistent and insistent so a degree of patience is essential. 'Learning' in the corporate setting runs on a steep curve: at first take off learning in a new task is slow; then, as skills are acquired, there is a rapid increase in units of output – in this case, environmental programmes and projects.

But the curve is experienced as steep: there is difficulty, friction and conflict as new priorities have to be accommodated alongside existing corporate goals. Remember the technical definition of the experience curve: it refers to the empirically observable phenomenon in which the

1 Focus on the corporate learning curve. Environmental goals need to be acquired and assimilated alongside financial, operational and personnel goals.
2 From the start, use positive audit to inject good news into the environmental programme.
3 Rely on, manage and use the technical experts. You are the client and represent the corporate interest.
4 Gain and sustain top management commitment from the start. Ensure that your successes are fully understood by top management and the external stakeholders of the business.
5 Make environmental audit part of the normal route to the top for ambitious younger managers.
6 When possible, convert environmental benefits into financial cost savings and investor attractiveness, and build these into the reporting cycle.
7 Admit mistakes and shortcomings and agree goals for putting environmental problems right.
8 Build environmental auditing into the reporting cycle and use this as a basis for dialogue with insurers, investors and community groups.
9 Set and achieve attainable short and mid-term targets, which can be publicised by key middle and senior corporate managers.
10 Build on environmental successes from the start. Every business has something right in its existing environmental performance.
11 Concentrate on discovering points where environmental performance can be converted directly into core financial and quality strategic targets.
12 Respect your critics and develop methods of working with their concerns.

Figure 3.1   Twelve principles for integrating environmental programmes into corporate strategy

cost per unit of a product declines by a predictable percentage each time a company's experience at producing and selling it doubles (Boseman and Phatak, 1989). The steepness of the learning curve reflects both the rapid increase in output and also the rapid increases in stress in affected areas of the organisation.

Finally, and this may take some time, the new system comes into stable balance. Increases in output fall into a more steady and sustainable curve. Stress decreases, as the new system of environmental programmes runs alongside financial, operational, personnel, distributional and other systems.

Principle 2   From the start, use positive audit to inject good news into the environmental programme
The environmental programme manager has a number of tools to decrease the stress and accelerate the learning curve. Positive audit is one of these. This approach seeks out existing good environmental practice in

the organisation, and gives it immediate recognition and publicity. By showing that existing good practice, however unplanned, is going to be recognised, the environmental manager shows management colleagues that the new approach will give proper credit and share good news, as well as inevitably targeting problem areas.

Positive audit is critical in the first phase of corporate environmental programmes. However, it continues to remain central in the later established phases, for it provides incentive for other managers, not those necessarily involved in the immediate programme, to implement innovative good practice and bring it to the attention of the programme. Thus, rather than being seen as an enforcer of bad news, the environmental programme becomes a facilitator of management recognition.

Principle 3　Rely on, manage and use the technical experts. You are the client and represent the corporate interest

The corporate environmental programme is first of all a corporate programme and then an environmental procedure. Environmental scientists – ecologists, ecotoxicologists, chemists, botanists, biologists and so on – have developed important skills which rely on scientific procedures and complex analytical protocols; their expertise and its deployment are critical to success in the corporate environmental programme.

At the same time, their work must be accessible to the corporate decision-making process and its consequences must be converted into meaningful improvement programmes. Not only must the corporate environment be made sustainable: so must the decision process through which corporate improvements are achieved. The legal and financial consequences of the new programme require the work of specialist engineers, lawyers and accountants.

Using all these skills, the environmental programme manager must manage the interrelationships between environmental problems and improvements. Therefore the capacity to co-ordinate experts and control their outputs, along the lines of the contractual procedures laid out in Chapter 8, is vital.

Principle 4　Gain and sustain top management commitment from the start. Ensure that your successes are fully understood by top management and the external stakeholders of the business

An environmental programme has behind it the fear of substantial legal, financial and corporate penalties. However, its success in the corporate internal setting is largely determined by its becoming perceived as a positive contributor to corporate success, rather than a negative bringer of bad news and destroyer of profitable businesses. This means that the externally driven necessity of corporate environmentalism must be transformed into the internally driven desirability linked to environmental products, successes and investor confidence.

Other businesses and agencies can similarly undertake to transform their worst environmental businesses into their best. The environmental manager is key to this process.

Principle 5   Make environmental audit part of the normal route to the top for ambitious younger managers

The nature of top management's commitment to, and identification with, the corporate environmental programme will partly be linked to the amount of energy they see coming into the programme from younger managers in the organisation. Younger talent should be targeted and recruited to the corporate environmental programme. The environmental unit can then be seen as a growing component of the organisation.

Seek out secondments: that is, temporary reassignments of younger management specialists from legal, accounting, finance, product development and operations sections of the organisation. Show them how to use their expertise in achieving environmental targets. Give them opportunities to develop special projects with various operations groups in the organisation and to use the results in publicising new environmental successes.

Principle 6   When possible, convert environmental benefits into financial cost savings and investor attractiveness, and build these into the reporting cycle

The corporate environmental programme is both a method of internal operational change and a process of external cultural alteration. The values of environmental corporatism have traditionally been remote from, and add-ons to, the priorities of financial and strategic management, but with the new consumer and legislative environment, environmental objectives are becoming central both to financial and to strategic change. Such issues as the avoidance of possible liability suits are becoming priority issues. During the 1970s car manufacturers were faced for the first time with legal action on behalf of dead or injured persons put at risk by unsafe car designs. During the 1980s asbestos and other industrial carcinogens were brought to the fore as major hazards for which, in spite of legislative gaps, companies were to be made financially liable.

During the 1990s every industry, including many service industries, will be made potentially liable for unforeseen consequences of unsafe environments or products.

For each plant and product in the company, the corporate environmental programme should establish the potential legal and financial consequences if potential consumers or the environment are harmed. The notional financial benefit can then be placed against the real cost of taking preventative action. This part of corporate reporting is, of course, confidential within the company. Some of it can be, and is being, converted into effective public communications, as was shown in many newspaper stories during 1991.

For instance, car manufacturers may conceivably be held indirectly responsible for the greenhouse effect, which is largely produced by carbon dioxide, a major emission of both petrol and diesel engines. The current drive towards zero-emission vehicles is triggered not only by competitive and legislative pressures, but also by the potential threat of consumer and environmental interest groups taking action. If car manufacturers are found to have been less than committed in pursuing emission reduction and elimination, they may then be potentially liable for direct and indirect damages. Figure 3.2 shows a notional cost–benefit comparison for this issue.

Cost	– $10 billion for a programme of increasingly low emission engines.
Benefits	– Avoidance of consumer damages totalling potentially $50 billion. – Transformation of the consumer image of the product family and the industrial sector from environmentally damaging to environmentally benign. – Continuation of product liability insurance and reinsurance facilities.

Figure 3.2   Possible costs and benefits of an environmental strategy for car manufacture

The impact of such an environmental strategy would be significant. From being perceived as the most massively damaging product family to the environment, cars would be transformed initially into environmentally neutral products, with the ultimate aim of turning them into environmentally beneficial products. Could their engines in the end emit only environmentally benign outputs?

Principle 7   Admit mistakes and shortcomings and agree goals with corporate critics for putting environmental problems right

Admitting mistakes in public is one of the more recent developments in corporate communications strategies for major public agencies or business organisations. It is comparable to President Ronald Reagan's 'Teflon' approach to political mistakes: agree that a mistake has been made, and then link the problem to joint action to put the mistake right.

Such agreement is essential, particularly for organisations with a long industrial history. For instance, sick building syndrome is now a well-established problem in buildings with defective or infected air conditioning or air circulation systems. It also stems from inadequate turnover of air, airborne chemicals from new furniture or fittings and a prevalence of smokers in inadequately ventilated environments. Action against the company may be brought by employees' trade unions, or consumers or government agencies if a substantial number of cases of illness can be traced to such building problems.

Affected employers can choose to fight these actions, but the publicity will affect both their business reputation and their attractiveness as a responsible employer. To dismiss or deny the existence of problems carries potential penalties in terms of loss of business. Insurance consequences are also paramount in this calculation. It is better to establish any such problems through a jointly designed environmental audit and to negotiate a series of changes over a number of years to lower the occurrence of, and exposure to, such risks. Although the costs are high, they can be carried forward in pricing policies, an aspect of capital investment.

Principle 8   Build environmental auditing into the reporting cycle and use this as a basis for dialogue with insurers, investors and community groups.

Information is power in the corporate environmental programme. The quantity and quality of information made available by the corporation to the public and investors leads to judgements being made about both the organisation and its environmental unit. Therefore, the environmental manager must have a clear understanding of which parts of the total information system are shared with external stakeholders in the organisation.

There is every reason to believe that corporate candour with investors, insurers and communities will, in the long run, bring about a degree of trust and joint action that a history of misrepresentations cannot. Problems that are recognised and managed are seen as problems on the way towards solution. Therefore, an organisation that presents its environmental shortcomings as problems on the way towards solution instils a degree of certainty that otherwise will be missing. This allows potential investors, acquirers and customers to feel that they are dealing with a responsive and dynamic entity capable of innovating its way through difficulties.

This is the pattern now being established by all the major multi-nationals in Europe and North America. Environmental concerns are no longer seen as peripheral but as central in the next generations of product and corporate strategy. Stock market and insurance valuations are reflecting this: Union Carbide is now seen as a 'green' company; MacDonalds is rapidly improving its environmental image; and the most successful UK retailer of the early 1990s is Body Shop, run by philosophers and ecologists who openly advocate breaking through traditional market research ('modelling of past behaviour'), into strong value statements where products are tied to the whole course of planetary social, cultural and biochemical evolution. It is this value-driven corporate ethos which will define the corporate strategy of the new century.

Principle 9   Set and achieve attainable short and mid-term targets, which can be publicised by key middle and senior corporate managers
The principle of setting and attaining achievable benchmarks is at the heart of transforming long-term environmental goals into short-term successes. For instance, the UK government has set a 10-year goal of recycling 50 per cent of household refuse. However, its one-year goal is to recycle about 1 per cent more than at present, because this is the achievable goal, given the present technology and commitments within reach of the waste management system.

For local government, such goals are essential. To move various environmental projects into high gear requires early successes which are warmly recognised by top management: incremental successes year by year are achievable in such areas as the recycling of paper, use of recycled paper, promotion of low-emission public vehicles, and energy-conserving building strategies. These targets and the degree to which they have been attained should be published in annual reporting cycles and given prominence in the performance assessments of managers.

Principle 10   Build on environmental successes from the start. Every business has some good aspect of environmental performance at the beginning
The initial audit of an organisation will establish where its environmental

strengths and weaknesses are. The strengths should be given equal or greater prominence over the shortcomings, right from the start. For instance, individual school managers may, of their own volition, have successfully insulated older school buildings in recent years. Such small efforts should be given recognition.

Too often the environmental movement has been seen and has seen itself as a counter-culture, establishing anti-industrial and anti-technological alternatives to the mainstream of contemporary society. This must change, if consumption and production patterns are to be effectively influenced. Mutual recognition is growing between the one-time critics and the managerial groups with responsibility for large organisations. By recognising the important environmental progress which has taken place, for instance, in terms of energy conservation in fleet management, or in the development of better engines, there is great opportunity for the new strategic approach to be quickly adopted.

Principle 11   Concentrate on discovering points where environmental performance can be converted directly into core financial and quality strategic targets

This principle is the most difficult one to achieve, for implementation of environmental measures usually means that something is lost: investment is taken away from other priorities and costs of production rise. However, two main points need to be considered.

1   New product lines can come from redefining waste as a saleable by-product. A classic case is the conversion of sawmill waste into chipboard and other wood products which now form a major product family in the timber industry.
2   Prices to customers can be raised, sometimes to a premium if a green product is perceived as inherently more desirable than its competition.

Principle 12   Respect your critics and develop methods of working with their concerns

The notion of open communications between an organisation, and its critics and stakeholders, is not new in the environmental era. However, it reflects the enormous increase in sophistication, curiosity and commitment felt across the whole of the information economy (Naisbitt and Aburdene, 1990). The truth is therefore much more sought after and is much more likely to be made public than at any previous time in business history. Managing information flows across corporate boundaries is very much part of the environmental manager's responsibility, alongside that of his or her public relations colleagues. This management process is best seen as a sharing of problems, and an exchange of views and interpretations, rather than as a confrontation between critics and defenders.

Characteristically the key to this process is the phrase, 'We agree that we share a problem in this particular area.' That is, the problem is owned not only by the company but also by its critics. Although it may be mainly the company which has to undertake mitigation, the external critics are necessarily brought into an exchange of information, rather than of accusations.

During the early 1990s, Greenpeace, the leading international environmental group, has become a leading corporate member of the emergent environmental industry. Greenpeace has established formal consultancy links with both government and industry, and carries out its own business planning. Inevitably there has been a decline in deep green guerilla tactics, as it has become increasingly apparent that the organisation's views were taken seriously and were highly valued by the previous defenders of the status quo.

In 1989, when Greenpeace found that its success had produced a huge membership increase and consequent increases in funds, it built a new corporate headquarters on the north edge of the City of London; it is a 'green' office building and a meeting centre for the environmental movement. The radical success of earlier stages in the organisation's development is succeeded by a coolly rational attempt to improve existing practice, similar to other businesses.

These 12 principles summarise much of the procedural and planning elements which follow in Parts II and III of this book.

THE IMPACT OF ENVIRONMENTAL AUDITING ON CORPORATE STRATEGIC MANAGEMENT

The corporate environmental programme can be applied principally through audit procedures, and may affect some main strategic areas. The following categories of strategic management are now discussed: corporate strategy; business strategy; and functional strategy (see Boseman and Phatak, 1989). For each category, the following headings will be used: key concepts, main decisional choices, and environmental strategy input.

Corporate strategy

Key concepts

At the senior level, the organisation must decide on the precise nature of the business it is in. Then it must determine whether this business allows it to achieve optimal or acceptable levels of profitability and growth. The organisation must also consider possible new businesses which might better achieve its objectives. Resource availability in its all its forms – manpower, supplies of raw materials, location, distribution, capital, management skills – must be incorporated into the corporate strategy.

A principal classification scheme used in recent decades has been the product portfolio matrix: the best-known versions are the BCG Growth–Share Matrix and the GE Business Portfolio Matrix (see, for instance, Boseman and Phatak, 1989, for a useful discussion of portfolio theory). Environmental concerns and impacts may alter the relative attractiveness of businesses and therefore change them from cash cows to dogs: for instance, as recently as 20 years ago, asbestos was still used in the manufacture of materials. However, asbestos is now known to be carcinogenic, and asbestos products are no longer used.

A *Financial Times* news item on 23 October 1991 (p. 6) demonstrates the long-term difficulties in moving away from industries like asbestos:

> US asbestos ban rebuffed. A federal appeals court in New Orleans has rebuffed a wide-ranging ban by the US Environmental Protection Agency on the use of asbestos in the US, stating that the agency need to provide more support for its ruling, reports Nikki Tait from New Orleans.
>
> The EPA ban was initiated in 1989, and was due to take full effect in 1996. The Agency's lawyers had claimed that the long-range health benefits would be considerable; asbestos is a suspected carcinogen, and has been blamed for various lung problems, especially in workers exposed to the material.
>
> The ban was being challenged by various business interests involved in the asbestos industry. In its ruling, the three-judge panel of the 5th US Circuit Court of Appeals said that the EPA failed to offer opponents of the ban sufficient opportunity to cross-examine witnesses regarding disputed facts, when hearings on the proposal were under-way.

Main decisional choices

The key variable is the allocation of resources between all the business activities in the organisation.

Environmental strategy input

It is clear that, for many organisations, product lines and activities that were objectively attractive prior to the passing of environmental legislation, have become less so afterwards. An example is the production of damaging chemicals such as CFCs, whose permissible levels are being drastically reduced by international treaty. However, other product lines, such as agricultural fertilisers, impose indirect environmental costs which can in many cases no longer be cost-effectively managed without major reinvestment. In many cases only very large firms with long lead times and substantial capital can make the necessary changes.

Alternatively, there may be a fragmentation of markets into tighter niches where many smaller firms can make acceptable products and compete on favourable terms. For instance, the production of marine-friendly boat hull cleaners in the 1980s established such a market. This market was not large enough to attract the big suppliers and thus opened many marketing opportunities for smaller startup companies.

Business strategy

Key concepts

Once a company is committed to a particular business or product area, it must decide on how to be most competitive in that area. This will depend greatly on the nature of the business: whether it is rapidly growing or stagnant; highly or barely profitable. The objective is to make the organisation profitable given its situation. For instance, a small firm in a low-growth sector may still have profit opportunities from supplying low-cost products against higher-cost larger producers.

Main decisional choices

The principal concern in any organisation is to direct its resources in such a way that its position is sustained and has a chance to grow within the market of that business area. Specific business functions are critical here: marketing; finance; human resources. The main focus of the strategy is to maximise resource productivity: synergy and the development of distinctive competencies are thus key strategy components (Hofer and Schendel, 1978).

Environmental strategy input

An emphasis on environmental compliance and a strong corporate environmental charter fully incorporated into strategy will alter the shape of business in a short time. In some cases the firm may be able to advertise 'environmental friendliness' for its goods or services. In other cases, implementing the findings of the environmental audit may lead to specific costs which need to be examined and built into the product.

But the most important opportunity arising from the input of an environmental strategy is to translate newly non-permitted environmental by-products into marketable end products.

Functional strategy

Key concepts
Each of the specific functional areas of the business – production, operations, distribution, finance, marketing, human resources – must be organised to be consistent with the overall corporate mission.

Main decisional choices
Corporate leaders must ensure that all senior functional managers are fully committed to the central corporate and business strategies. They must seek detailed evidence that functional areas are being planned in ways that are synergistic with the central business objectives.

Environmental strategy input
Changes in the environmental codes affecting the company, or the adoption of an environmental charter, need to be reflected in the functional and operational strategies. This has particular importance as discrepancies between overall announced aims, and local deviations and avoidances, are noted in the press and can damage the credibility of the overall environmental strategy. Thus coherence and synergy within any announced environmental strategy is of enormous importance to its chances of success.

A CHECKLIST FOR CORPORATE ENVIRONMENTAL PROGRAMMES

Internal targets

Does the environmental programme:

- effectively use the financial, human and physical resources of the firm?
- link to the broad strategic plan for the organisation?
- reflect the personal values of senior managers and employees of the organisation?
- have a direct relationship with market expectations and the organisation's internal capabilities?
- provide sufficient flexibility?
- take advantage of the planning, managerial and developmental capabilities of the organisation?
- emphasise the company's internal strengths and improve its weaknesses?
- reflect the financial resources of the company?
- provide appropriate and achievable targets, and a milestone programme of attainable successes, as well as some more stretching targets?

External targets

Does the environmental programme:

- further the company's compliance with environmental standards?
- advance the company's reputation with its customer base for good environmental practice and environmentally friendly products?
- assist the organisation in confirming or taking market niches?
- improve competitive conditions for current or planned product lines?
- help the organisation to use or take advantage of existing market and product strengths?
- assist the enterprise in entering new product areas which make it better able to establish good environmental performance?

SUMMARY

A wide range of corporate strategic issues will be affected by the adoption of a corporate environmental programme. Questions of acquisition, development, decline and disposal will now all be subjected to environmental audit, as well as to financial and corporate audit. The methodologies of Parts II and III provide a detailed view of how to bring an environmental programme into being through internal procedures. This programme will become over time, like other aspects of business management, a routine aspect of business development and evaluation. None the less it will be full of opportunity, challenge and complexity for the ambitious manager.

Notes

1 Transnational companies are contrasted with multinationals by the formers' cross-border integration of operations and management. Multinationals, on the other hand, may have an assembly of holdings in several countries, but a relative lack of integration of operations. In a few cases, there is no transfer of financial profits between parts of multinational operations, with profits being retained for reinvestment only in the local economy. The ultimate benefit for the home corporation comes only at the final sale of the overseas company. Transnationals have complex banking and treasury management methods for ensuring that funds can flow among subsidiaries as required.

PART II

Business Strategy and Development of the Corporate Environmental Programme

This moves from business missions arising out of environmental strategies into specific techniques by which corporate environmental programmes are established.

Chapter 4 specifies the objectives of corporate environmental programmes. It details procedures for establishing an environment unit, and lays out a typology of audit activities.

A detailed guide for carrying out audit activities is suggested in Chapter 5, with particular links to the EC's draft Directive on Eco-Audit and the British Standard on Environmental Management Systems.

Chapter 6 focuses on public-sector applications of environmental audit, with a detailed case covering an English county council. Public and governmental enterprises have a broader environmental role, inasmuch as their purposes and missions by definition involve concern for the larger setting in which they carry out their activities. Over time, therefore, they should become exemplars of good environmental practice, both in procedure and in results.

4 DEVELOPMENT OF, AND TECHNIQUES FOR, CORPORATE ENVIRONMENTAL STRATEGY[1]

THE CORPORATE ENVIRONMENTAL PROGRAMME

A corporate environmental programme can be defined as a timed programme of environmental improvement for an organisation, specifying objectives, procedures, programme evaluation protocols, dates and quantitative measures for environmental action. This may take the form of such formal policy statements as:

- environmental charters;
- environmental codes; and
- environmental missions.

The corporate environmental programme also generally includes statements concerning targets and resourcing. The programme is thus both a policy statement and an operational plan for carrying out the objectives of the mission (code, charter). Figure 4.1 shows linkages between the corporate environmental programme and the management process.

STARTING A CORPORATE ENVIRONMENTAL UNIT

The procedure used for developing a corporate environmental unit is shown in Figure 4.2. The development of a corporate environmental unit, like the development of other business units, involves six essential elements:

- product specification;
- process;
- marketing;
- distribution;
- finance; and
- administrative systems[2].

Environmental strategy process	Review of all existing environmental corporate strategy	Formulation of corporate environmental baseline	Establishment of environmental charter	Determination of environmental strategy	Implementation of environmental strategy	Control of impacts
					Environmental audit/assessment specification	
Integrative procedure						
Strategic management process	Assessment of organisation strengths, weaknesses, opportunities and threats (SWOT)	Formulation of organisation mission	Formulation of organisation philosophy and policies	Determination of strategic objectives	Implementation organisation strategy	Control of organisational strategy

Source: Adapted from Boseman and Phatak, 1989

Figure 4.1 A model of environmental strategy and its relationship to strategic management

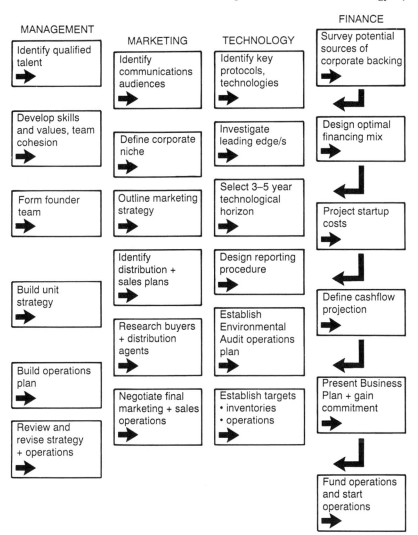

MANAGEMENT

MARKETING   TECHNOLOGY

FINANCE

MANAGEMENT	MARKETING	TECHNOLOGY	FINANCE
Identify qualified talent ➡	Identify communications audiences ➡	Identify key protocols, technologies ➡	Survey potential sources of corporate backing ➡ ↩
Develop skills and values, team cohesion ➡	Define corporate niche ➡	Investigate leading edge/s ➡	Design optimal financing mix ➡
Form founder team ➡	Outline marketing strategy ➡	Select 3–5 year technological horizon ➡	Project startup costs ➡ ↩
Build unit strategy ➡	Identify distribution + sales plans ➡	Design reporting procedure ➡	Define cashflow projection ➡ ↩
Build operations plan ➡	Research buyers + distribution agents ➡	Establish Environmental Audit operations plan ➡	
Review and revise strategy + operations ➡	Negotiate final marketing + sales operations ➡	Establish targets • inventories • operations ➡	Present Business Plan + gain commitment ➡ ↩
			Fund operations and start operations ➡

Source: Adapted from Venture Technology Project, IMRIC University of Greenwich 1983, Version 8.2, 1990, Registered (see notes 2 and 3)

Figure 4.2 Development of a corporate environmental unit

The corporate environmental unit's manager will simultaneously develop business plans and procedures in each of four areas:

- management, including products and processes;
- marketing and distribution of the product, focusing on both internal and external issues;
- technology; and
- finance.

Using a sequence of plans developed within a nucleus management team, a new environmental unit can be established that is capable of rapid growth.

Fundamentally, the new unit is in the equivalent position of a business which must rise or fall on its capacity to produce and market its 'products' effectively. Its key features should thus be flexibility and comprehensiveness. In this respect it should use state-of-the-art business modelling software.

ENVIRONMENTAL AUDITING

Environmental auditing has three broad aims:

- compliance with regulatory codes;
- assistance in acquisition and disposal valuations; and
- corporate development towards green missions.

Figure 4.3 shows the broad characteristics of these three objectives.

There are many different types of audit, depending on the type of business being audited, the reason for the audit, and the depth and breadth of the audit. These audit types include:

- corporate audits, which consider the workings of the entire corporation;
- activity audits, which consider one activity of the corporation;
- site audits, which consider a single installation;
- compliance audits, which test industry compliance with relevant environmental and safety standards;
- risk audits, which consider safety, occupational health, and/or risk to employees and the public;
- production audits, which trace energy and/or materials from their entry into the corporation to their exit; and
- acquisition/divestiture audits, which test environmental liabilities that could arise from those activities.

General category	Specific areas
Compliance	– Legal conformity – Anticipated conformity with liability for new regulations – Review of mitigative and ameliorative programmes

Acquisition/ disposal	– Sale of facility
	– Acquisition of facility
	– Valuation/appraisal of property for:
	  – insurance
	  – loan security

Corporate development	– Monitoring of corporate environmental policy and procedures – Establishing baseline for development of 'green' corporate environmental programmes – Assessing control system adequacy – Implementing and reviewing corporate environmental programme measures (mitigation and remediation) – Assessing risks in unregulated areas – Improving product or process quality through response to environmental impacts (especially buildings, landscape, large engineering works)

Figure 4.3   Environmental audit objectives: general typology

Broadly, however, audits can be divided into two categories.

1 Cyclical auditing programmes, where auditing occurs on a scheduled cycle of occurrences. This form of audit will be a central product of an environmental unit. It may be carried out by specialists drawn from inside the company or from outside consultants.
2 Single audits for special purposes. These are more likely to be done by outside consultants.

The environmental audit process calls for a flexible and iterative process that, at its most comprehensive form, encompasses the following.

• A baseline study of the existing situation;
• A decision on the scope of the audit;
• Early identification of options for environmental change. These must respond to environmental considerations without jeopardising core corporate objectives; nor should corporate objectives endanger environmental goals. Actions to improve environmental consequences may be of three types:
  – ameliorative options, whereby negative impacts may be lessened in either quality or quantity;

- mitigative options, whereby the negative impacts may be balanced by other actions which lessen or reduce its impact; or
- compensatory options, whereby the negative impact may be tolerated in return for other forms of action to relieve damage.

- A systematic assessment of options. There must be a protocol for determining and assessing environmental options and their effects, as well as related corporate consequences. In environmental audit, as in other corporate programmes, option appraisal is carried out to determine the relative attractiveness of different approaches. An option appraisal matrix is a concise method of arraying and distilling choices for decision, and for comparing their costs and benefits within a brief context. These appraisal matrices are discussed in further depth in Chapter 8.

- Careful sifting of options. All the facts, values, analyses and interpretations must be reviewed to focus on the most relevant factors and issues. The emphasis must be on significance: which choices can lead towards a positive environmental outcome within the context of other considerations?

- Continual refinement and fine-tuning of the audit. Over time, new factors and considerations will be identified in relation to different options. There must be a method by which new findings are brought into the appraisal of options throughout the option appraisal process.

- Accurate and objective reporting to decision-makers. Findings and observations must reflect:
  - the best available technical knowledge of pertinent factors and issues, and their implications; and
  - an accurate synthesis of the views, perspectives and values of different stakeholders within and outside the business.

- Timely and accurate public disclosure to stakeholders who have key powers in the decision-making process and to the public. Reporting corporate experience to the public allows for greater public understanding and the advancement of the science of audit. Indirectly, it benefits the business by establishing its reputation as a contributor to environmental improvements.

- Diligent monitoring. During implementation of the chosen option(s) there must be systematic verification, to test predictions and to permit useful and timely adjustments to the environmental strategy.

- Timely adaptation and refinement of the corporate system. Environmental monitoring and auditing may require the alteration of a plant's operation or of the design of a new installation.

- Systematic evaluation of the audit procedure.

Clearly, environmental audit is part of a business' overall corporate decision-making process. By placing environmental objectives alongside other objectives, such as those related to finances and production, the audit system is knitted into business operations.

Two case studies of Environmental Audit follow: both are site-specific audits carried out by outside consultants for private companies.[4]

ENVIRONMENTAL AUDIT CASE STUDIES

Chemical production facility

In May 1990, Travers Morgan were invited to undertake an acquisition audit of a chemical production facility in the north-west of England. The factory had been producing a variety of chemicals for many years, including solvents, acids, pigments and compressed gases. The factory was situated in a heavily urbanised area, and was adjacent to domestic properties and various local amenities. In addition, a water course ran alongside the site. The costs of the investigation were shared between the vendor and the possible buyer.

The study was conducted by three environmental scientists under the direction of a senior environmental engineer. Strict time limitations were imposed due to the negotiations concerning potential purchase of the site. A draft report was required to be produced within 15 days of instruction. Discussions on various aspects of the project continued until the acquisition was formally announced.

The audit comprised a walkover assessment of current activities on the site, chemical testing, analysis of company records, meetings with various statutory and regulatory authorities, and continued liaison with legal representatives of the clients. The instructions from the clients and the responses to them were made available to both parties simultaneously. The study included the assessment of potential contaminant migration from the site by reference to company records. Details of site operation were assessed and a review of the site history was prepared.

A key part of the investigation was an assessment of compliance, both historically and currently, with legislative controls relating to emissions to all environmental media and issues relating to the health and safety of site personnel. A review of relevant legislation was prepared for the client and compliance with these requirements assessed. In conducting the walkover survey of the site consideration was given to current operational practices; where potential non-compliance with regulatory requirements was identified ameliorative measures were recommended.

As the investigation was designed to assess both existing and potential environmental liability associated with site operation, reference was made to all relevant statutory authorities. Each authority was invited to comment on existing consent compliance and any proposals for modifying existing consent conditions. No significant compliance problems were identified nor significant modifications to licence agreements proposed.

The investigation of the site included excavation of 15 trial pits to obtain samples of soils and groundwater for subsequent chemical analysis. Two aspects of chemical contamination were assessed from these samples:

- factors which may affect durability of buildings and infrastructure; and
- factors which may result in the migration of pollutants from the site into the surrounding environment.

Analysis of samples revealed the presence of contamination which could result in both of these effects. Aggressive ground conditions were identified which would necessitate the use of protective measures to all subsurface concrete structures. Off-site migration of contamination was also anticipated due to the presence of elevated concentrations of various contaminants in the groundwater at 0.5–1 metre below ground level.

Further investigation of groundwater movement within the site was undertaken. Following the investigation remedial measures were designed to improve groundwater collection and land drainage within the facility. Due to the operational status of the facility the available options for control of groundwater movement were restricted. Various engineering solutions appropriate to reducing the migration risk were proposed and evaluated for consideration in the detailed negotiations between the clients.

The acquisition was completed and it is understood that certain of the remedial measures recommended are being undertaken.

Waste transfer station

M.J. Carter Associated were commissioned by Shanks and McEwan (Southern) Ltd to undertake an independent comprehensive site audit of the waste transfer station at Hendon, London. The site occupies approximately 2.6 hectares and processes up to 1,200 tonnes per day of solid household, commercial and industrial wastes. The aim of the audit was to assess the aspects of control and monitoring of the facility which relate to the environmental quality at the site and the surrounding area. These aspects were compared with regulatory standards and the company code of practice.

Two members of M.J. Carter Associated's technical staff undertook the audit. A telephone call was made to the site manager explaining the reasons for the audit and a letter was sent detailing the information needed to undertake the audit, namely:

- a detailed plan of the facility;
- copies of the planning permission and site licence;
- operational working plan;
- details of monitoring procedures and monitoring results;
- waste disposal arrangements;
- details of the final disposal points of all wastes;
- maintenance records;
- schedules of environmental control and landscape works;
- waste disposal authority site inspection reports;
- any other reports *re* environmental investigations; and
- any correspondence with the public regarding environmental nuisance.

The information received prior to the audit visit was assessed to identify aspects of the operation warranting detailed scrutiny during the visit. The site plan indicated the presence of a residential area adjacent to the site, and it was deemed necessary to devote part of the visit to assessing the impact in terms of nuisance on residents of that area. It was also apparent that one working day would be sufficient to undertake the audit visit.

Prior to entering the site on the audit visit, a reconnaissance was made of the surrounding area to identify sensitive locations for which environmental monitoring procedures may be needed, providing data against which to assess the environmental monitoring regime at the waste transfer station. An inspection was made of all information available, and an inspection was then undertaken of the facility to assess the adequacy of environmental controls and monitoring procedures.

The inspection of the facility revealed that considerable efforts had been made to design a structure and yard layout which would cause minimum environmental disturbance, especially at the sensitive locations to the east of the site. The most significant deficiency was the lack of an oil interceptor in the surface drainage system in the site yard.

The monitoring procedures at the facility were generally considered adequate and were rigorously implemented. It was noted, however, that there was no procedure for the regular inspection of the oil interceptors in the foul water drainage system from the waste transfer hall, or of the surface water gullies in the site yard. No arrangements were made to monitor noise at the sensitive locations adjacent to the site, although occasional monitoring was undertaken of noise levels within the facility. The facility is designed so that vehicles discharge wastes directly into the compactor hoppers, so there was no suitable opportunity to inspect adequately the majority of waste.

Following the site inspection, the site manager was informed of the preliminary conclusions and recommendations of the audit team, thus allowing him to put into effect immediately any of the recommendations that he considered warranted such action. A detailed report was written describing the site and its surroundings, and assessing the design and operation of the facility, and the environmental control and monitoring procedures. Recommendations were made for improvements to the surface water drainage system and for the instigation of monitoring procedures for the surface water gullies, foul water system oil interceptors and noise levels at sensitive locations.

In addition to identifying the potential for improvements in operating procedures, the environmental audit provides a guide for assessing any future alterations to operational procedures.

ENVIRONMENTAL ASSESSMENT

In contrast to environmental audit, which concerns the existing operations of a firm, environmental assessment focusses on the impacts of future proposed developments on the environment. In most developed and many developing countries, environmental assessment is legally required before planning permission can be given for large-scale proposed developments: these include power stations, highways, bridges, industrial plants, retail and office centres, housing developments and extraction sites. Each of these must be assessed for its impacts on air, water, soil, wildlife habitats, noise and other aspects of the physical setting. Often, environmental assessments also address the social and economic impacts of the proposed development.

In the EC, the preparation of environmental assessments has been mandatory since 1988, when the Directive on the Assessment of the

Effects of Certain Private and Public Projects on the Environment (85/337/EEC) became operational. The various Member States have established separate regulations to carry out the provisions of the Directive. In the US, environmental assessments have been carried out on federal projects (excluding most defence projects), since the National Environmental Policy Act of 1969. Other countries, including Canada, China, Australia, Japan and Brazil, have regulations or guidelines requiring environmental assessment.

These assessments are presented as supporting documents, often with extensive technical detail, which must accompany applications for permission to develop a particular site. Their costs have added a new element to the risk money which must go into major project proposals, both from the private and the public sectors. Some countries require environmental assessment to cover the impacts of their home-based transnational companies on other countries.

Recently, requirements for assessing or auditing government policies, plans and programmes have been proposed. So-called 'strategic environmental assessment' (SEA) is already required in some public-sector organisations such as the US Department of Housing and Urban Development (1981), the State of California (1986) and the Governments of The Netherlands (1990) and Canada (1992 proposed). The Commission of the European Communities (1991) is working on a draft Directive on SEA. It is likely that SEA will become much more widespread in the coming decade; this would have a strong impact on environmental auditing in public sector organisations.

Environmental assessment affects only a tiny proportion of the total built environment, that which is proposed for creation in the near future. But it is these new developments which attracted the earlier round of environmental legislation. New projects are potentially more disruptive of what British law calls 'the quiet enjoyment of one's home' (or business or community) than a continuation of existing plant or building.

An environmental assessment case study follows.[5]

CASE STUDY
Kansai International Airport

Construction of the Kansai International Airport near Osaka, Japan began in 1987 and is scheduled for completion in 1993. The airport will be located on a 511-hectare reclaimed island connected to the mainland by a

3.8 kilometre road/rail bridge, and will cost about $8.5 billion. It is expected to replace the Osaka International Airport, which is located in a densely populated area and has been the focus of numerous complaints and lawsuits about noise. 'Aeropolis', a community to service the Kansai International Airport, is being built on 318 hectares reclaimed from the mainland near the airport.

Planning of the airport took place in three stages:

- decision concerning the airport's location;
- decision concerning construction methods to be used; and
- prediction and mitigation of specific impacts.

At each stage, a report was prepared explaining the key factors leading up to the decision, and environmental factors considered.

In 1968, Japan's Ministry of Transport proposed seven sites for the new airport: one on land and six on reclaimed islands. A committee of 17 academics, industrialists and government officials was set up to consider the merits of those sites. Three sites were rejected because they were too close to urban centres, and two others were merged into one. The remaining three sites were then compared, based on the following criteria:

- convenience of access;
- flight capacities;
- environmental impacts;
- ease of construction;
- co-ordination with local fishermen's rights;
- co-ordination with local development plans; and
- positive economic impacts.

Each of these criteria was given an importance weighting, where the criterion considered most important – convenience – was weighted about three times as heavily as the least important – economic impacts. Each of the three sites was then rated according to how well they fulfilled each of the criteria. Finally, the importance weightings were multiplied by the fulfilment ratings and added up for each site to determine the preferred location for the airport. A report explaining these findings was released in 1974.

Four methods of construction were then considered for the chosen location.

1 An island made of four side-walls which would then be filled to the top

with soil from nearby hills. This represented the best-known technology at the time.

2 An island with high side-walls but with a lower central platform; the aeroplanes would land into the topographical equivalent of a baking tray. This would allow less earth to be used during construction.
3 A platform built on top of concrete pillars rammed into the bay bottom.
4 A 'floating island' anchored to concrete pillars.

The last method was considered to be the least environmentally damaging, the first method the most damaging. In the end, the committee opted for the first method on the grounds of cost-effectiveness and safety. A report of 1980 outlined these findings.

In 1984, the Kansai International Airport Company Ltd was established as Japan's first private share-issuing company to construct, own and manage an airport. According to both Japan's national and Osaka's prefectural guidelines, the company was required to prepare an official environmental statement which considered the environmental impacts of the proposed airport and how to mitigate these impacts. The environmental statement, which was published in 1986, considered the following impacts:

construction	*operation*
noise	noise
air quality	air quality
water quality	water quality
marine life	currents
shipping	marine life
	safety
	land animals
	scenery
	electricity
	shipping

Planning permission was granted in late 1986 and construction began a month later. No one single full environmental statement was prepared for the Kansai International Airport during the 18 years of planning, but the sum total of the three reports is equivalent to one. The comprehensive consideration of environmental issues, alongside social and economic considerations during the planning of the airport is a good example of environmental assessment.

Notes

1 Since 1981 the Venture Technology Project of the University of Greenwich Business School has conducted research on, and philosophical exploration of, the dynamics of technology industry formation. About 50 bankers, venture capitalists and government policy planners have been interviewed, as well as the managers of 5 small British and American startup enterprises. An earlier version of these findings was reported at the UK Management Education and Development Association conference at Ashridge, England in January 1985. Financial support for this project came through funded research assistantships of Thames Polytechnic and the Inner London Education Authority from 1983–5.

2 These six categories for business planning are based on the American and British work of Albert S. Humphrey and his predecessors, first at Stanford Research Institute during the 1960s and later at Business Planning and Development, London and St Louis. The set is registered under the name Team Action Management, and is the method employed by Albert Humphrey, to whom we are indebted for the use of these topics.

3 The enterprise development process is a procedure used for developing millionaire-producing enterprises. Its key features include the simultaneous development of increasingly more refined business plans and procedures in each of four areas: management; marketing and distribution; technology; and finance.

4 The authors are grateful to Travers Morgan, M. J. Carter Associated, and Information for Industry Ltd. for permission to use these case studies. The case studies were previously printed in *Environment Business* (1991).

5 This case study is taken from Barrett and Therivel (1991).

5 A MODEL PROTOCOL AND INTERNATIONAL STANDARDS FOR ENVIRONMENTAL AUDIT

This chapter discusses the proposed EC Directive on Eco-Audit and the British Standard on Environmental Management Systems, both of which are likely to have a profound impact on environmental auditing in future years. It discusses links between them, and to other relevant legislation, including the UK Environmental Protection Act 1990 and BS 5750 on quality systems. It proposes an environmental auditing protocol with advisory comments. On the basis of this protocol, an environmental manager can devise, with adjustments for local circumstances, a procedure for carrying out an environmental audit in his or her own organisation.

EC DRAFT ECO-AUDIT DIRECTIVE

The EC's 'Eco-Audit' Directive will make environmental auditing a voluntary but regulated activity throughout all Member States. It applies directly in all Member States; in other words, it does not require Member States to pass enabling legislation. The legislation features a voluntary system for the introduction of environmental auditing and is targeted primarily at manufacturing and processing industries.

Once a company decides voluntarily to seek registration for an eco-audit, it agrees to abide by the rules on a site-by-site basis. Participating companies must do the following.

1 Undertake a comprehensive environmental review of their activities, impacts and regulations, which includes the following topics:
   - management;
   - saving and choice of energy;
   - raw materials;
   - water;

- selection of production processes;
- planning;
- design;
- packaging and transportation of the product; and
- communications with the public.

2 Prepare or refine a detailed environmental policy, programme and objectives. This includes:
   - a company environmental policy, i.e. broad intentions of the company with respect to the environment;
   - a company action plan;
   - objectives and targets – objectives will usually be broad-brush (e.g. reduce SO_2 emissions), targets will be quantified and attached to a timescale (e.g. 10 per cent SO_2 reduction in two years); and
   - an environmental programme or strategy to achieve this (e.g. install scrubbers).

3 Put in place an environmental management system to deliver this package. The system organises people, documentation, equipment, systems, monitoring etc. to ensure that the strategy is carried out. It includes regular audits at sensible frequencies.

4 Prepare a statement according to eco-audit rules, setting out objectives and background. This statement includes:
   - a description of the company's activities, as relevant;
   - an assessment of the relevant environmental issues, including factual data;
   - a summary of quantitative data on the organisation's emissions, waste, raw materials, energy and water consumption during the period before the report;
   - company policy, plans, targets for the site;
   - an evaluation of environmental performance at the site; and
   - an agreed deadline for the next statement.

5 Get the statement verified, and submit it to the competent authority. This provides assurance to the public that statements are fair and gives credibility to the whole scheme. Verification entails confirmation that the factual part of the statement is true and fair, that results reported are correct and that no significant issues are omitted. It also entails confirmation that reports are based on adequate environmental audit procedures and that the necessary management system components exist. The verifier should not, however, repeat the audit process.

Registration is achieved once the audit statement is validated by an accredited verifier, and is received by the competent national registration body. The company is then registered and entitled to use the logo. The logo only refers to the site that the company has submitted for eco-audit. It does not refer to the company as a whole unless the company had submitted all its sites and holdings to the eco-audit process.

In order to remain registered, the company has to perform the audits as promised in the first statement and submit statements outlining the audit results. De-registration occurs if a registered organisation fails to provide a verified audit statement by the date previously agreed. There is no judgement by the competent body of the 'quality' of the company's environmental performance.

Figure 5.1 presents the main features of the EC's eco-audit scheme. The role of the external verifier and the need for standardised criteria, protocols and procedures are key to the eco-audit regulation, to ensure that a level playing field exists across the Single Market. Owen and Mundy (1991) comment:

> A wide range of factors will be considered, from the procurement of raw materials to the use of energy and the disposal of waste. In assessing the overall impact and the relationship that an industrial installation has on both man and the surrounding environment, the proposals represent a radical departure from the current forms of EC pollution control which are sector-specific and aimed only at particular pollutants. The frequency of the audits (probably annual) will mean that a company's compliance with the rules and regulations and its policy and management systems relating to areas such as pollution discharge, choice of raw materials, waste management and product planning will constantly be under review. Not only will they cover current environmental performance, but they should also stimulate improvements in a company's management.
>
> European legislation on the environment has developed to such an extent that many of the data-gathering exercises of environmental audit already have to be undertaken to ensure compliance with other legislation such as the UK Environmental Protection Act 1990. Nevertheless, eco-audit takes the concept of environmental responsibility of firms a step further. It forces firms to review all their activities from resource use to disposal (from cradle to grave) in an environmentally sensitive manner.

Objectives	– Systematic, objective and periodic review of environmental performance of certain industrial activity – Provision of information to the public
Sectors to be covered in initial phase	– Mining, quarrying – General manufacturing – Production of electricity, gas, steam, hot water – Solid or liquid waste recycling – Waste treatment, destruction, disposal – Other commercial activities could be included under a pilot scheme
Registration	Voluntary, based on individual sites
Validating authority	To be designated by Member States
Compliance	Once registered, companies would be obliged to comply with the eco-audit scheme in full; entitled to use a logo so testifying
Elements of eco-audit	– Planning – Review of environmental programmes – Assessment of organisation and equipment – Identification of areas for improvement
Stages of eco-audit	– Internal – Validation by independent expert; this stage would have specific detailed rules and protocols to be adhered to and harmonised across Member States
Areas of focus	– Energy management – Waste reduction, recycling – Raw materials and water savings – Accident prevention
Publication	Company required to publish annual 'environmental statement' for submission to national authority and general public

Figure 5.1   EC draft Eco-Audit Directive: principal aspects

THE BRITISH STANDARD FOR ENVIRONMENTAL MANAGEMENT SYSTEMS

Organisations faced with the cost of implementing environmental programmes often seek to gain some benefit or advantage from implementation. One such benefit is certification of the successful implementation through a government agency such as the British Standards Institution (BSI). In 1992, the BSI adopted its own environmental management systems standard based on a talk by Michael Gilbert (1992). This standard may well form the basis for a similar standard by the International Standards Organisation (ISO), the global agency which has emerged in recent years. Therefore, it is useful to examine the BSi approach in detail, as this approach will no doubt serve as an important international prototype in coming years.

Broadly, the BSi uses performance standards in environmental audit which spell out expected outcomes for:

- each part of the auditing protocol;
- the final outcome of the protocol's operations; and
- the various forms and systems an organisation may use in achieving the required standard.

The British Standard is in three parts:

- Part 1 introduces the concept of the standard;
- Part 2 specifies the elements of the system; and
- Part 3 is a guide to the specification, designed to give more detailed information about the specification requirements.

The procedures of the British Standard entail the following steps.

- A *commitment* by the organisation to establish an environmental management system.
- An *initial review* and assessment of the organisation's environmental position concerning its environmental policy, adherence to environmental standards etc.
- Formulation of an environmental *policy* in the form of a corporate environmental programme. It is this environmental policy which will be the basis for a statement of *targets and objectives* towards which the environmental management system will strive.
- An *inventory of the organisation's activities*, and an *assessment of the activities' environmental impacts*, consistent with the stated policy.
- An *inventory of pertinent regulations and requirements* to ensure compliance.
- The development of an *environmental management plan* and of a supporting *manual* which details all relevant parts of the system.
- The application of the management plan in both the company's *operations* and *record-keeping*.

- A cycle of *audits* of the company's performance to test whether objectives and targets are being met.

Part 1 of the standard focuses on 'concepts, elements and applications'. Covering matters similar to the EC's eco-audit provisions, the standard details the costs, benefits, risks and rewards of establishing an environmental management system in a firm. Consistent with the view taken by many observers, the BSI standard emphasises that environmental management is integral to the organisation's management system. In particular, issues of health, safety and quality assurance are interlinked and implicit in environmental standards.

The standard's aims are summarised as follows;

> . . . to facilitate:
> (a) the achievement and demonstration of compliance with environmental regulations and with organisational policies which establish more stringent requirements;
> (b) effective use of personnel skills and other resources;
> (c) accreditation schemes for environmental management.

In adopting this standard, an organisation will thus aim to accomplish two objectives:

1 sustained achievement of environmental performance necessary to meet the requirements of its environmental policy, including compliance with regulatory requirements; and
2 provision of confirmation to its own management that the intended environmental performance is being achieved and sustained efficiently.

Figures 5.2 and 5.3 show respectively the organisational model and the life-cycle model based upon the British Standard.

Part 2 of the standard deals with specifications for the development, implementation and maintenance of an environmental management system. The key performance standard for Part 2 is as follows:

> The organisation's management shall define and document its environmental policy. The management shall ensure that this policy is understood, implemented and maintained at all levels in the organisation.

The need for in-company verification procedures is inherent to this. An important standard is that:

> . . . investigations of incidents and accidents, and of resulting corrective actions, shall be carried out by personnel independent of those having direct responsibility for the work being performed.

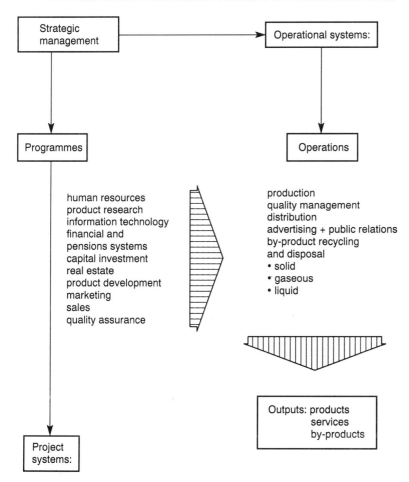

Figure 5.2   Organisational model for Environmental Audit

Source: IMRIC University of Greenwich Business School 1992.

Provision for inventories, audits and reviews of all aspects of environmental systems are established. Procedures include standards for three different operating modes: normal operating procedures; abnormal operating procedures; and incidents, accidents and potential emergency situations.

The inventory of environmental systems must include compositions, quantities and paths of releases to air and water, and of wastes generated; consumption of materials, fuels and energy; and effects upon specific

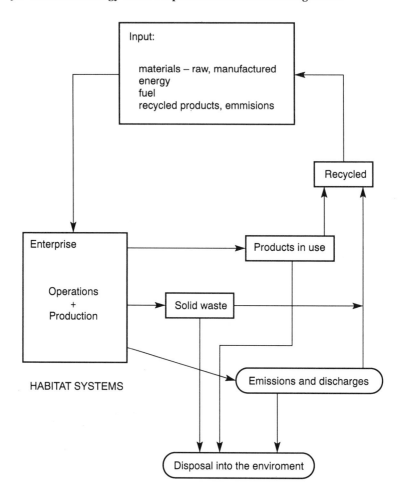

Figure 5.3   Life-cycle model for Environmental Audit

Source: IMRIC University of Greenwich Business School 1992.

parts of the environment and ecosystem, including the workforce and workplace.

Internal environmental audits will focus on whether the operation of the environmental systems are bringing them into line with the organisation's adopted environmental plan. The audit will be conducted by following a protocol, which will involve the use of:

- questionnaires;
- checklists;
- interviews;
- measurements; and
- direct observations.

Part 3 of the standard focuses on additional details of implementation and verification. It discusses different responsibilities of management, reporting systems, training and other details which need to be specified when applying for BSI certification.

In sum, the BSI standard allows an organisation to gain public recognition for the expensive and painstaking implementation of 'environmental management systems'. This recognition may be important both in assisting compliance, and in achieving maximum efficiency in insurance arrangement, and acquisition and disposal planning. Importantly, while the BSi standard requires many details of provisions, its specification allows for a wide array of different mechanisms in arriving at the required standard.

LINKS BETWEEN BRITISH STANDARD 7750 FOR ENVIRONMENTAL MANAGEMENT SYSTEMS AND BRITISH STANDARD 5750 ON QUALITY SYSTEMS

The British Standard for Environmental Management Systems is closely linked to, and complements, BS 5750 on quality systems. BS 5750 was adopted in 1979, was updated and adopted as an International Standard (ISO 9000 series) in 1987, and has been adopted by the European Committee for Standardisation as the EN 29000 series.

The major difference between the proposed Standard on Environmental Management Systems and the Quality System Standard is that currently the Quality System Standard addresses the organisation's outputs as products or services of the organisation, and tries to establish criteria for the management system of the organisation that will meet customer needs. The Standard on Environmental Management Systems, on the other hand, focuses much more on the by-products or product or service delivery, with the customer being less easy to define, namely the general public.

The European Organisation for Testing and Certification would have to establish a common protocol for assessment and certification to fulfil the requirements of both standards. This would ensure that assessment and verification against proposed standards would be carried out in a common way. The regulation would cover a multitude of environmental issues that the environmental management system should be addressing. To meet these requirements an organisation would need to take a holistic view of its operations to focus on those areas that are most important in terms of environmental impacts.

To develop an environmental management system, the company would carry out assessments of all of its activities to decide which are the most important from an environmental point of view. Implicit in the proposed legislation is a cradle-to-grave approach to the environmental effects of companies' activities. Upstream the organisation would need to examine where raw materials and manufacture materials come from. Downstream, what happens after the product or service leaves the organisation in terms of its 'in use' effects and disposal would be the centre of analysis. The company would then come to a judgement about where to focus its environmental effects analysis, and its plans and programmes related to product lifecycle.

LINKS BETWEEN EC DRAFT ECO-AUDIT DIRECTIVE AND BRITISH STANDARD FOR ENVIRONMENTAL MANAGEMENT SYSTEMS

It is intended that the proposed EC Eco-Audit Directive and the British Standard for Environmental Management Systems are co-ordinated activities which link to one another. This reciprocity ensures that the standard requirements are compatible with the legislative requirements of environmental audit regulations. The British Standards Institution is confident that this approach will enable UK industry to have at their disposal a national standard which sets the scene for the development of international standards.

There is a close similarity between the two. The EC Directive includes four key areas that are relevant to the proposed BSI standard.

1 The requirement for participating organisations to establish an *internal evaluation of the environmental management system*, the output of the system being a defined and achieved level of environmental performance. An element of the system is the organisation's evaluation of the

system's effectiveness by self-assessment or internal audit. Most organisations will integrate this into their existing management system as part of the way they run their business.

2 The system will have a *common approach*. It will start with the *company's policy for performance* and, from that, policy objectives and targets for management and operations will be identified. This will be summarised into a plan. At the lowest level these are work instructions that are integrated into the way people actually carry out their day-to-day job, be it on the production line or in services or management. Day-to-day operations are translated into control, testing, verification and measurements; all those things that are normally necessary to ensure that work instructions are being appropriately followed to meet requirements.

3 On a regular basis *operations will be reviewed* to ensure that they are meeting objectives and targets. There will be a need to consider at the very senior level whether the policy that established the objectives and targets is appropriate. The company will draw on audit results at a high level to ensure that the policy and programmes are appropriate.

4 The regulation will require the preparation of a *public statement*. Thus, the results of the environmental audit and management review will need to be prepared in a summary report to be made available to the public.

The EC draft Directive does not specify the role of the external verifier. It does, however, need to be designed in such a way that external verification is achievable. In the British context, this means that the BSI standard must be written in the form of a specification, to enable the standard to be used as a way of facilitating EC legislation.

A MODEL PROTOCOL FOR ENVIRONMENTAL AUDITING: OVERVIEW

This section proposes a protocol for environmental auditing which combines the requirements of the proposed EC Eco-Audit Directive, the British Standard for Environmental Management Systems and best practice. In the remainder of Part II and in Part III of this book further operational specification are added, to assist in attaining increasingly better practice in the corporate environmental programme.

Figure 5.4 illustrates the basic stages in the model protocol. These stages are as follows:

1 *Set the context:* commit top management to an environmental mission, the establishment of a corporate environmental programme and environmental unit, and environmental auditing.

2 *Plan the audit:* prepare the audit team, determine the audit scope, identify background information, select methods for conducting the audit and define priority areas.

3 *Undertake the audit:* through questionnaires, interviews, site inspections.

4 *Evaluate findings:* describe impacts, establish links between them, assess their significance, explore alternatives, make recommendations.

5 *Report:* prepare and make available a summary of findings and recommendations to decision-makers and stakeholders. This report focuses on the most pertinent factors and issues required for informed decision-making.

6 *Implement action plan based on audit:* consider and implement changes to the organisation's operations and policies.

7 *Verification and feedback:* review the accuracy and impartiality of the audit, and propose future improvements.

The term 'operation' is used throughout the model protocol as a generic term for the wide range of activities that could be audited: policies, programmes and plans, site operations, plant, products, strategies etc.

This model cannot fit the vast diversity of cultural and strategic settings found across the hundreds of thousands of organisations undertaking these activities. It does, however, give a pattern which may be adapted to this variety. It generates a detailed system of observations and findings with which, by modification, managers can build up a detailed environmental audit procedure. Moreover, it provides a common reference point for internal and external environmental managers which can assist in negotiating the terms and conditions of the audit.

The term 'protocol' is deliberately borrowed from the laboratory sciences. It pertains in particular to rigorous tests or proofs which two parties in disagreement ('adversaries') can agree are reliable methods of arriving at mutually acceptable truth. In environmental audit such procedures are particularly important, in order that both managers and external auditors can have confidence in the quality of the information and findings.

A good protocol must start from the perspective that goodwill exists on both sides. As new compliance codes come into effect, all sides are motivated to ensure not only that temporary adequacy is achieved but

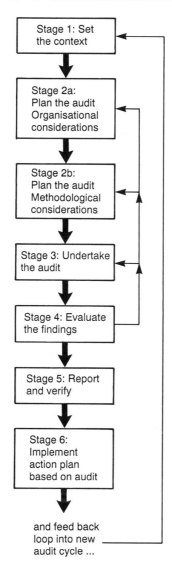

Figure 5.4 A model protocol for environmental audit

also that predictable risks have been assessed which may compromise the
financial, legal or liability position of the business at some future

date. Directors and employed or consulting experts can also be found personally responsible in future court cases.

In summary, the following key assumptions in protocol must be kept in mind:

- there is no one perfect model;
- information is always imperfect;
- incremental improvement in decision-making is the overall goal; and
- patient review and reinterpretation of existing data can often reveal as much as new collection of data.

Stage 1   Set the context

The investment of time and effort in laying the foundations for environmental audit can help to ensure that the audit can be conducted in a timely and efficient fashion, with good co-operation and an ultimately receptive and informed audience, inside and outside the organisation. There may be resistance to the imposition of the audit, which should be expected, as audit activities comprise both threats and opportunities for various people in the organisation. While audits can avoid costly and time-consuming surprises and problems downstream, they do impose new burdens on the planning and operational parts of the organisation. As well as extolling the virtues and necessities of environmental audit, the challenges, threats and difficulties should also be explicitly identified and addressed. Strategic networking, careful pre-planning and timely provision of required support can help to reduce anxieties and tensions, while promoting the teamwork vital to a good environmental audit.

- Gain top management commitment. Help establish environmental considerations on the normal 'agenda' of key managers and units responsible for corporate planning and development. Equip top management with appropriate knowledge, reference materials, environmental regulation, and policy documents and other briefing materials. Enhance their sensitivity to, and understanding of, environmental issues. Highlight linkages between environmental concerns and the core corporate objectives of the organisation.
- Establish a corporate environmental programme and an environmental unit (this is discussed further in Chapter 7). Make the organisation aware of the role and responsibilities of the environmental unit.
- Make environmental unit staff aware of the non-environmental aspects of the corporate context. Environmental auditors and their managers

need to understand and appreciate the organisational and political realities faced by strategic planners, and where the organisation's financial, social and legal responsibilities must be balanced with environmental considerations.

- Keep abreast of changes in environmental issues and regulations, and of comparable audits in other agencies and other strategy domains. Build networks with other units in the organisation, outside experts and other organisations to ensure that a ready capacity for planning and implementing audits is available on a stand-by basis.

Stage 2a   Plan the audit: organisational considerations

- Anticipate the need for environmental audits of:
  - newly acquired plant;
  - plant proposed for construction;
  - new investment programmes;
  - acquisition or divestment choices;
  - new corporate policies requiring major changes in the environment, e.g. expansion into national regulatory settings which have different environmental requirements from those of the home base.
- Review the scale and nature of the operation. The scope and level of effort of audit can vary considerably, depending on the anticipated scale and significance of environmental effects of the operation under consideration. In general, the more certain one can be about the environmental impacts of an operation, the more detailed and rigorous the audit can be. Conversely, if there is good reason to believe that the operation has no significant environmental effects, then a relatively cursory preliminary screening and audit may be all that is required. This would confirm initial assumptions and tentative conclusions.
- Establish the scope of the audit. Determine whether to audit the entire company; an individual site, department or process; or an issue of particular importance. Identify the kinds of technical issues involved, their scientific complexity and the level of existing knowledge concerning the operation's impacts on the environment. Determine how in-depth the audit should be, based on anticipated environmental effects and financial, time and technical constraints. Determine how long the audit will take, and how often to repeat it. In effect, even the decision of what level of effort should be applied to a audit constitutes a 'mini-audit' in itself.

- Determine stakeholders affected, their distribution, organisation and level of knowledge.
- Identify the auditing team, considering expertise and availability. Ideally, the team should comprise both environmental experts and people familiar with the workings of the operation being audited. Appoint a team leader. Allow the team to draw upon the expertise already existing in the company: this will not only improve the audit team's awareness of issues within the company, but will raise other employees' awareness of the audit and its associated issues.
- Identify the basic information, advice and experience that may be required for the audit. Identify contacts and sources that can meet these needs. If necessary, identify outside experts to round out expertise: ideally any outside help should be used as part of the in-house audit team. Chapter 8 proposes a procedure for agreeing on a contract with both in-house and outside audit staff. Commission necessary background research at the earliest possible moment, to assemble pertinent knowledge and data.
- Set up arrangements for consultation with top management and with site staff. Inform site personnel of the audits purpose. Set up arrangements for obtaining permission if needed.
- Anticipate special needs *re* resources, staff, time etc.
- Prepare an audit plan and schedule. Build requirements for the audit into work programmes. Anticipate and secure the resources required.

Stage 2b   Plan the audit: methodological considerations

- Gather relevant background information, including:
  - corporate environmental policy, charter, mission, strategy;
  - relevant planning documents, authorisations, monitoring records etc.;
  - relevant regulations and standards.
- Review the operation and its possible impact. Determine, to the extent possible, the form and nature of the operation, including such issues as product manufacture, distribution, timing, target markets and linkages with other operations. New operations, in particular, may present major new environmental impacts for the business. Environmental audit of major new operations should thus be addressed by more than one team, so that different and independent perspectives can be developed.

- Identify possible environmental impacts of the operation. A number of techniques for impact identification are described in Chapter 8. Define priority areas: carry out preliminary screening and ranking of anticipated impacts.
- Select appropriate methods for conducting the audit, specifying any special requirements or considerations in their implementation. Take into account:
  - the objectives of the operation;
  - the scope and complexity of the operation;
  - the nature and significance of the operation's environmental impacts;
  - availability and reliability of data and knowledge;
  - level of scientific and stakeholder interest in the new programme; and
  - priorities, timing and available resources.

  The selection of an audit method is a strategic decision that typically must be made on the basis of educated guesswork, tempered by experience. Plan and prepare appropriate checklists, criteria and frameworks for audit that meet the unique needs of the organisation. Establish a data-gathering system.
- Establish control procedures for the audit: define testing and verification strategies.

Stage 3   Undertake the audit

Based on the agreed audit method, data on the operation's environmental impacts are then gathered. Ensure that information is collected about all key aspects of the operation. Be prepared to gather additional information about issues which come to light during this stage. Ensure that data gathered are factual and objective.

- Review background/baseline information. Ensure that all relevant documents exist, are up to date and accurate, and comply with pertinent regulations. Ensure that the company policy is adequately carried out; consider possible changes to the company's environmental policy.
- Undertake a questionnaire of staff to determine their level of environmental awareness, their operating procedures, perceived environmental impacts and any suggestions for change. These questionnaires should be accompanied by a letter explaining the aims of the study and specifying a time limit for returning the questionnaire.

- Interview staff, remembering to:
  - schedule the interview in advance so that staff will be prepared and have time;
  - interview in the workplace so that the interviewee is relaxed, relevant material is easily available and the auditor sees the facility; and
  - use good interviewing techniques (e.g. observe the interviewee's body language, ask open-ended questions).
- Inspect the operation. Where a large number of variables in the operation's outputs and emissions are being audited, a representative random range of variables should be audited using statistical sampling techniques. This will require, among other techniques, stratified sampling and random sampling. Using the principle of marginal selection, the auditor can choose to audit those activities which are deemed to be marginal to the main process, and which may well be ignored by local management as being unlikely to be monitored. This could be:
  - vehicle management, where engine tuning and emission controls may be seen as marginal to the operations of the local plant;
  - office control of waste paper, where this is not a main waste output of the local operation; or
  - nuisance at remote areas of the site, including boundaries.

  Where such marginal audits are pursued, they must be undertaken in the same spirit as the inspections of the main operations.
- Apply testing/verification strategies.

Stage 4   Evaluate findings

This evaluation should comprise an analysis of whether the operation complies with all relevant environmental regulations; a description of impacts, their significance and linkages; an assessment of alternative operations; and recommendations for changes.

- Characterise and describe impacts, as discussed in Chapter 8. The list of impacts should constitute the widest possible range of characteristics, although in reality certain impacts will be either impossible to portray meaningfully or irrelevant for actual decision-making purposes.
- Establish a conceptual framework, in the form of a logic model, tracing all known or anticipated linkages from corporate strategy/policy to programme specifications to project/product/activity/service to

environmental impact. In some cases the linkages may be virtually certain. In other cases they may be more speculative, relying upon emerging theories and speculative hypotheses regarding environmental impacts of new operations. Wherever possible, the rationale for the linkages should be made explicit, and should highlight the approximate degree of certainty which can be attributed to the assumed linkages. This enables decision-makers properly to consider the relative strength of arguments regarding environmental consequences, whether positive or negative. It also enables the audit to be revised as new data, knowledge or validated theories emerge. Summarise the evidence and rationale for the logic model and its cause/effect linkages.

- Appraise the significance of the impacts. The significance of each impact will hinge on the precise nature of the operation and on the strategic context in which it functions. This is discussed further in Chapter 8.
- Consider the need for a more systematic and rigorous analysis of anticipated environmental impacts focusing on:
    - high-priority impacts, including those that may be significant for key stakeholder groups, biotic systems, or marketing/reception of the operation, where greater precision and thoroughness is important;
    - 'suspect' impacts, where assumptions and projections may have been crude and unreliable, and which require further testing and confirmation before they can be brought fully into the logic model; and
    - newly identified impacts, whose consequences have not been detected or given appropriate importance.

    Chapter 8 suggests criteria for determining whether a more detailed audit is needed.
- Explore alternatives to the operation; mitigatory, ameliorative and compensatory options that can help to minimise or offset anticipated negative impacts, or enhance the achievement of positive impacts. Ideally this should be achievable without significantly jeopardising core strategic or commercial objectives. Consider a range of optional configurations for the operation. Typically, these are developed with different performance and costings in mind; now they must also integrate environmental performance as a criterion when determining the preferred options. Chapter 8 discusses identification and analysis of alternatives.
- Assess the operation's future environmental performance, and that of the present operation which it is meant to displace. Appraise the

implications of the improvements measures in terms of:
- expected and potential environmental impacts;
- technical feasibility;
- financial implications;
- the stakeholders affected and their relative values, concerns and priorities; and
- strategic impacts on corporate aims.

Discuss these findings and implications both within the auditing team and within the company.

- Make recommendations, stating an estimate of cost, resource needs and an optimum time for their introduction, as well as their expected effectiveness. Where appropriate, these should be discussed with the personnel directly concerned to make them aware of proposed changes and to fine-tune recommendations, based on their experience.

- Ensure that the audit protocol documents are completed.

Stage 5   Report

The key challenge of this stage is to translate and interpret findings in ways that are relevant to the decision-makers. The audit report should be structured and written to make clear distinctions between options, high-lighting essential differences. Major issues and implications should receive the greatest attention, especially those for which there is mean-ingful choice or flexibility in approaches in strategy, design or operations. The report should identify issues requiring immediate decisions and attention, as well as those decisions which can be deferred, pending more information or experience at the subsequent implementation stage. The report should therefore indicate where decision-makers can set directions or conditions on subsequent implementation, while allowing progress to be made on the strategy itself. Finally, the report should identify issues requiring more specific audit at subsequent design and monitoring stages.

The environmental report and supporting documents should be written in clear language, avoiding unnecessary technical terms and jargon, keeping in mind that they must be read by a non-technical audience. Illustrations and case studies can help explain key points. The summary of findings should focus on the most essential factors, eliminating or playing down minor issues. Only data that help illustrate or explain a particular point should be included.

- Write up draft findings and recommendations in the form of a draft audit report. This report forms the core of the environmental audit's output. The format that is generally most useful consists of:
  - executive summary (one to two pages);
  - a statement of the objectives of the audit;
  - exposition of the methods used to conduct and verity the audit;
  - presentation of key information;
  - analysis of information, using objectives and identified methods;
  - main findings and conclusions; and
  - recommendations.

  Following the main body of the report will come:
  - references used;
  - technical appendices; and
  - other supporting materials identified as relevant.

  Prepare an executive summary for the board, which includes clear recommendations for action.
- Circulate the draft audit report and request comments, to ensure adequacy. Where possible and appropriate, provide a live briefing or presentation of the audit report for decision-makers and/or interested stakeholders. This may be taped for presentation to other audiences.
- Gain board approval of the report and recommendations.
- Prepare final findings. Where required, produce a public document summaring the audit report. This should include as much information as possible within the strictures of commercial and political confidentiality. This document will form the basis on which external stakeholder groups, not directly involved in the decision, will trust the quality of the audit report and the decision-making setting. Therefore, it is not a minor output, but is in itself a major component of the process.
- Prepare and assimilate background materials supporting the environmental report. This will explain the rationale, sources, methodologies and related issues which support the audit. It will also assist in subsequent evaluation and audit initiatives.

Stage 6   Implement action plan based on audit

Environmental audit does not end with the preparation of the report. Indeed, the report is a starting point, triggering a sharing of information and ideas. It should focus discussion and debate into a decision-making mode.

Intervention in the implementation process is, strictly speaking, not part of the audit process. However, it is a vital link that determines the relevance and effectiveness of the audit process. The process of intervention can also be used as an evaluative tool to develop better understanding about linkages between strategy and projects. Thereby intervention can improve the ability to forecast possible environmental outcomes. It can also build an understanding of factors and forces that may require the strategy to be modified.

- Address significant impacts first.
- Determine the need for intervention in strategic and project implementation. Assist in the translation of the audit recommendations into changes at different levels:
  - objectives and targets in an environmental management plan;
  - corporate environmental programme;
  - appropriate design and implementation guidelines.

Stage 7   Verification and feedback

An investment of time and effort in evaluating substantive and procedural lessons learned can improve the knowledge base and methods for environmental audit. Monitoring and evaluation of the audit findings will:

- determine if outcomes matched predictions;
- assess the need for intervention to cope with unforeseen effects;
- determine if a reappraisal of design or strategy is warranted, in light of unforeseen or adverse outcomes; and
- ensure the collection of information that can assist future design and strategy formulation and their assessments.

By sharing the results with other parties, organisations can build valuable networks of allies whose knowledge, data and experience may help in future planning and audit initiatives.

- Appoint a verifier/monitor.
- Plan and carry out monitoring and follow-up processes, considering:
  - key issues and factors in implementation;
  - threshold indicators for intervention – unforeseen environmental impacts, restructuring of strategy or design, reappraisal of implementation;

– priority areas for long-term environmental evaluation, leading to knowledge useful in future environmental audits.

The monitoring should focus on the most critical elements of strategy or design, i.e. those with the greatest potential positive or negative impacts and especially those which were most subject to uncertainty during the audit. Monitoring should be structured to test specific conditions and circumstances within which the design was implemented, thereby allowing a comparison with the underlying assumptions upon which the strategy or design was based. This allows consideration of other factors such as:

– cross-impacts of other operations or strategies;
– scope for intervention, mitigation, amelioration or compensation;
– reappraisal of the strategy/product in light of actual outcomes.

- Evaluate the audit. Compare anticipated outcomes and effects with actual results. Summarise and analyse mitigating factors and circumstances that may explain variances between anticipated and actual outcomes. Come to conclusions regarding:
  – the accuracy and appropriateness of the audit and factors that contributed to its success or shortcomings; and
  – implications for future strategic assessments, including new understandings regarding linkages between specific strategies and environmental impacts, and suggestions regarding improved procedures.
- Consider the future use of alternative audit methods.
- Plan the next audit, incorporating recommendations from this one.
- Evaluate and improve the criteria used to evaluate the audit.
- Share the above with appropriate stakeholders and decision-makers.

SUMMARY

Auditing requires a balancing of facts and values, on a case-by-case basis, using appropriate input from both professional experts, and the affected workers and communities. Unlike scientific field research or financial audit, environmental auditing does not involve the application of hard and fast rules which dictate inclusion or exclusion in each and every case. Instead, it involves a creative, case-by-case development of specific audit designs, arising from discussions and agreements with decision-makers and stakeholders. Decision-makers and stakeholders must agree on findings separately for each case; these will be placed alongside other important concerns in the political or corporate arena, and a final decision will then be arrived at as a reflection of the balancing of many aspects.

That said, environmental issues in coming years will function both as compliance imperatives and ethically desirable end-states. Grave legal and financial consequences may result from corporate decisions which ignore the results of environmental auditing.

6 ENVIRONMENTAL AUDIT IN THE PUBLIC SECTOR

This chapter examines the role and process of environmental audit in national and local government, and in other public sector organisations. The differences between public and private sector environmental audits are discussed. Existing policies for environmental audit in the public sector are reviewed. Procedures for managing a public sector audit are presented, based on the model protocol given in Chapter 5. Finally, an example of environmental audit in a public sector organisation is given.

ENVIRONMENTAL AUDIT IN THE PUBLIC VERSUS PRIVATE SECTOR

The role of environmental audit in the public sector differs considerably from that in the private sector. First, government agencies are responsible for setting and enforcing environmental standards and legislation; thus they act as protectors of the environment. They can require, or encourage, the production of environmental audits from public and private organisations, and set standards which the audit must achieve.

As part of their responsibilities as environmental watchdogs, public sector organisations are expected to set an example. For instance, environmental audits and assessments prepared by public sector organisations are generally expected to be at least as good (objective, thorough, sensitive to public opinion) as those prepared by private sector organisations.

At times, this may lead to a conflict of interests when a public agency has to regulate itself. The traditional resolution of this 'poacher–gamekeeper' problem has been to divide the agency, assigning the provision and regulatory functions to the separate parts. This has recently happened in the UK with the formation of the National Rivers Authority (NRA); the NRA now regulates water quality, while the previously existing water authorities have become responsible only for water provision. Similarly, the UK Environmental Protection Act of 1990 established a framework for separating the provision and regulation of waste disposal facilities.

In other cases, governments' environmental activities are monitored by an independent and neutral agency. In the US, for instance, the Council for Environmental Quality was set up by the National Environmental Policy Act in 1970 to act as an independent and neutral arbiter of environmental disputes, including disputes concerning the adequacy of environmental statements. The Netherlands have a similar council.

Public sector organisations have greater responsibility towards the public than do private firms. The primary responsibility of private firms is towards their stakeholders, in the form of maintaining and enhancing the firm's financial viability. Public agencies, instead, are responsible to all sectors of the public, and their objectives are considerably more complex: these include environmental and social goals such as equity, environmental sustainability and the provision of a wide range of services, all at minimal cost to the taxpayer.

As a result of this public responsibility, government and other public organisations must make greater efforts to engender public participation in their decisions, and to communicate the results of their activities. In environmental auditing, this involves getting public input in the early scoping stages, during data collection and when deciding on policy changes as a result of the audit, as well as making the audit findings publicly available.

Public sector organisations generally deal with more activities, different activities and with greater control than do private firms. Public agencies are responsible for the provision of such infrastructure as transport and waste disposal facilities, and with services such as law enforcement and education, which differ in type and scale from the product of most private sector organisations. Their 'product' is thus likely to be more diverse, and to affect more aspects of the environment, than that of private firms.

Finally, public agencies are affected differently by the political climate than are private companies. A change in the ruling party is likely to affect the priority and funding given to an environmental audit. Arguments about the financial benefits of an audit are less likely to succeed in the public than in the private sector; conversely, if an audit is seen as being politically beneficial, it may go ahead even if it cannot be shown to have an obvious financial return.

FORMS OF PUBLIC SECTOR ENVIRONMENTAL AUDIT

For these reasons, environmental audits by public agencies are quite different from, and less varied than, those of private firms. They are generally comprised of two parts.

1 A comprehensive review of the existing state of the environment in the area, usually in conjunction with a review of how well the state of the environment meets environmental objectives such as ambient air/water quality standards or land use projections. This 'state of the environment report' is often set up as a database which is continually updated. Figure 6.1 gives a possible list of topics for inclusion in a state of the environment report.

2 A systematic and objective evaluation of the environmental performance of the public sector organisation, and a discussion of changes needed to achieve the environmental objectives, given the current state of the environment. This is termed a 'policy impact analysis'; Figure 6.2 gives a possible list of topics for inclusion in such a document (G. Dean in Thompson and Therivel, eds, 1991).

- Environmental structure (geology, soils, climate etc.)
- Air quality
- Water quality
- Noise
- Land use (agricultural, forestry, etc.)
- Landscape and townscape
- Wildlife and habitats
- Open space and recreation
- Transport
- Waste production, treatment and disposal
- Energy production, consumption and conservation

Figure 6.1   Topic areas for inclusion in a state of the environment report (adapted from Associations of County Councils, District Councils and Metropolitan Authorities, 1990)

A great advantage of public sector environmental audits is that they are generally publicly available; this contrasts with private sector audits whose results, for commercial reasons, are often kept confidential or are only made public in restricted circumstances. Previous public sector

General
- existing environmental policies and objectives
- mechanism and structure for co-ordinating environmental issues and inputs from all departments
- mechanism for monitoring the implementation and effectiveness of the audit

Buildings
- energy consumption and efficiency
- building materials and design
- estate management
- waste management and disposal

Transport
- transport policies
- management of organisation vehicles

Office management
- use, conservation and recycling of resources
- domestic products
- furniture and fittings
- health and environment in the workplace

Finances
- purchasing policy
- investment policy
- development of 'green' investment portfolio

Education
- consumer advice and protection
- environmental education
- involvement and co-operation of staff

Land management
- land use polices and implementation
- environmental enhancement and conservation policies, and their implementation

Figure 6.2   Topic areas for inclusion in an environmental policy analysis
(adapted from Associations of County Councils, District Councils and Metropolitan Authorities, 1990; and R. Jarman in Thompson and Therivel, eds, 1991)

audits can thus be used as examples (positive or negative) for other public sector audits in a way which is not possible in the private sector.

POLICIES FOR PUBLIC SECTOR ENVIRONMENTAL AUDIT

Environmental auditing of public sector activities is not mandatory, and no official requirements for such audits exist. However, various groups have proposed guidelines specifically for public sector audits. This section reviews some of these. It does not review guidelines that are primarily applicable to private sector audits: these were discussed in Chapter 1.

In the UK, the Associations of County Councils, District Councils and Metropolitan Authorities (1990) have proposed a methodology for environmental auditing of public agencies. This includes lists of topics to be addressed in the state of the environment report and the policy impact analysis, as well as suggestions for managing the audit. Friends of the Earth (1990) have proposed similar guidelines which cover background information and general conditions, the structure of the audit and the selection of auditors; they have also proposed an Environmental Charter for Local Authorities.

Since the early 1970s the federal government of Canada, in Ottawa, has taken a key role in the development of both national and international environmental standards for government. Responding both to public pressure and political opportunity, the government has carried out a series of increasingly sophisticated reviews of its operations and environments to ensure that any negative impacts were being mitigated and that positive influences were being assisted. An early indication of this was a federal cabinet ruling in 1974 that federal properties were to be developed and managed so as to maximise the 'social, economic and environmental benefits to local communities'. By 1992 a formal guideline had been proposed for the environmental assessment of all federal policies, projects and programmes. At the same time, environmental audit of federal operations and facilities was being adopted in stages by various ministries.

In the UK, the first local authority audit was prepared by Kirklees Metropolitan Borough Council in conjunction with Friends of the Earth. Since then, at least 25 more local authorities have prepared to conduct or have actually conducted an audit. The audit prepared by Lancashire County Council is held up as being particularly good, but was also particularly expensive at more than £200,000 (G. Dean in Thompson and Theival, 1991).

MANAGING A PUBLIC SECTOR ENVIRONMENTAL AUDIT

This section applies the principles of managing an environmental audit given in Chapter 5 to a public sector setting.

Setting the context, planning the audit

An environmental audit of a public agency is likely to cover a wide range of topics, be comprehensive and be subject to considerable public scrutiny. It is likely to take at least a year, and to cost somewhere between £20,000 ($35,000) and £300,000 ($500,000). In other words, it is a drawn-out and expensive process, and not to be undertaken lightly.

The decision whether or not to proceed with an environmental audit will usually begin with the public agency's planning or environmental department, and will be finalised by its executive committee. The decision is more likely to turn around political than financial issues.

Friends of the Earth (1990) suggest that:

> the study should be commissioned and supervised by an environmental monitoring unit composed of officers of each department of the authority, with representatives of local environment and amenity groups, and the private sector . . . The study should not be the sole responsibility of one department.

An early decision is whether to perform the audit using in-house staff or to contract it out. An in-house audit is the cheapest option, and benefits from the agency staff's inside knowledge of the area and the operations of the organisation; such an audit is also easy to manage and monitor. On the other hand, appropriate and experienced in-house staff may not be available, and an in-house audit is likely to be biased by the agency's culture. An audit prepared by external consultants is likely to be more expensive and less easy to manage, but will also be more objective and ensures that the auditors have adequate experience. Variants on those options could include the formation of a new specialist in-house auditing team, or a combined team of in-house and consultant auditors (Associations of County Councils etc., 1990). Friends of the Earth (1990) advocate the use of consultants for reasons of independence and objectivity.

Regardless of who does the actual work, an in-house supervisory team will be needed to manage the work and report progress periodically to the appropriate committee(s). If a consultancy performs the audit, the supervisory team will also have to co-ordinate meetings between the consultants and in-house staff, and facilitate the consultants' access to data. Do not underestimate the amount of time and energy needed to do this.

The objective, scope and timing of the audit then need to be specified, and a contract drawn up. The agency must decide whether to concentrate on only those aspects of the environment over which it has direct control, or whether to expand the audit's objectives (and contents) to give it an educational and lobbying role. Public participation should be encouraged at this stage; a public meeting will not only help focus the audit on the topics of greatest concern, but may identify sources of information and local environmental expertise as well.

Undertaking the audit

The state of the environment report is primarily a compilation of already-existing information on environmental parameters (see Figure 6.1), topped up with data collected in the field, where warranted. However, this is not necessarily an easy task. It begins with identifying who has the information, and gaining access to that information; the latter may take longer and be (even) more frustrating than the former. The search for data should extend beyond governmental or quasi-governmental organisations, to local amenity or conservation groups, educational institutions and informed individuals.

It is then very possible that the information will not be in the form that would be most useful; it may not involve the precise area or timescale of concern, may be too sketchy or overly precise, or may not exist at all. Careful interpretation and recalculation, and topping up by fieldwork may be necessary. Finally, the information must be sensitively analysed: emphasis must be put on the more important issues, not on those for which the most information exists; the report must not overemphasise quantifiable data at the expense of descriptive information; and it must remain unbiased.

The policy impact analysis is even more difficult to carry out. It involves becoming familiar with the agency's policies and working practices (see Figure 6.2), determining their environmental impacts and proposing changes that might make them more environmentally beneficial. Consequently, the policy impact analysis takes considerable creativity, expertise and political acumen.

The analysis should start with a review of policies, staff activities and staff suggestions: methods for doing this would include preliminary discussions with department managers, questionnaire surveys of staff, and more in-depth interviews and/or discussions with staff. Instances of best existing practice should also be identified and publicised.

Friends of the Earth (1990) have proposed a matrix approach for identifying the environmental impacts of policies and activities. Environmental parameters are listed on the horizontal axis of the matrix, relevant policies and activities are listed on the vertical axis, and their interactions are described in the appropriate cells. A second matrix could be prepared for alternative policies and activities that are more environmentally beneficial. Chapter 8 discusses impact identification matrices in greater detail.

Reporting

When preparing the audit document and reporting its results in a public sector setting, the major difference is the much greater need for public accessibility and participation. The audit report will be read by a wide range of people, from specialists to interested local residents. Consequently, it must strike a balance between scientific rigour and public accessibility. It must be made publicly available, eg. in local libraries and agency offices, and it should also be available for purchase to interested parties at a reasonable cost.

The preparation of a non-technical summary report is particularly important. This summary report should be made even more widely available, preferably at no cost. Many people will read only the summary report, and will base their opinions of the entire audit on the quality of this summary, so accessibility and a lack of perceived bias are vital.

The public should be encouraged to respond to the audit findings; an address for correspondence should be included on the main and summary reports, and public meetings should be scheduled to discuss the report's findings. These public comments will identify topics of particular concern, and may bring to light difficulties or omissions in the report, which should then be addressed.

Implementation

The report itself, and any feedback from the public and concerned groups will then be considered by the appropriate committee. Again, the decision of what actions to take as a result of the audit will involve a balancing of the consultants' expert opinions, the public's wishes and the decision-makers' political priorities.

Monitoring

Like private sector audits, public sector audits should be continually updated, reviewed and monitored. The establishment of a computerised database during the initial audit will facilitate such updating considerably. However, the practicality of this will be again limited by financial and political considerations; the initial audit may have been prepared in response to a burst of public interest and enthusiasm, while monitoring may seem less attractive.

CASE STUDY
Oxfordshire County Council

Oxfordshire County Council's Environmental Audit had its origins in mid-1989, and was completed in July 1991. This case study discusses some of the key issues involved in preparing the audit. It is based on a talk given by Oxfordshire's chief executive, John Harwood (1991).

In the middle of 1989, a motion was put forward by a number of Oxfordshire county councillors on a wide range of environmental issues, and in November of that year the county council resolved to prepare an environmental action plan. A key part of this plan was that an environmental audit should be commissioned 'to form the basis for action to reduce pollution, to be monitored and regularly updated'.

In the early stages the county council experienced a major division of views about the aims of its environmental audit. One side wanted to limit the audit to an analysis of what impacts the county council, as a business activity, has on the environment. The other camp felt that the council's role as a local government required a wider remit for the audit. In the end, it was decided that the audit should look at the whole of the county and at all issues affecting the county, even though the county council does not have specific statutory responsibility for some of the issues addressed, e.g. water and air quality.

The environmental audit was overseen by both management and political structures within the county council. The Environmental Issues Sub-committee of the Policy and Resources Committee advised both that committee and others on issues related to the audit. A separate high-level interdepartmental officer management committee, which has representatives of all departments on it, deals with matters pertaining to the environment: this committee met once every month while the audit was being put together, and had the main responsibility for writing the brief and communicating with consultants. Finally, the county's environmental coordinator was the main day-to-day link between the consultants and the various county departments, and co-ordinated the county's data collection and its response to the various drafts of the audit.

The 1989 environmental action plan also led to a conference on environmental issues held in County Hall in Spring 1990. Over 100 people from a wide range of local environmental organisations attended, and explored the issue of what constitutes the environment in Oxfordshire, and what the county council could and should do about it. This helped to finalise views of what was wanted from the audit, what information could be obtained and what should be done with the audit.

A brief then had to be written for the consultants who would prepare the audit. However, this raised a problem: in order to write the brief, the county council needed to know something about the environment in Oxfordshire. It had to specify what was wanted without knowing the answer to the question. The conference was found to be helpful for this, as well as the results of previous pioneering audits, such as that of Kirklees. Indeed, as more environmental audits are prepared, people are likely to find this step easier.

Another issue at this point was achieving a balance between being specific and being vague. If the brief is too specific, one will get answers to all the questions that were asked, but one risks not getting answers to questions that should have been asked but were not. On the other hand, if the brief is too vague, one might not get the audit at all. A balance also had to be drawn between facts and what one might call 'understanding': why things happen, how they happen, why others don't and so on.

The brief was three or four pages long. It gave a list of issues that the county council specifically wanted information on:

- land use;
- landscape;
- open space;
- forestry;
- wildlife;
- agriculture;
- noise;
- air quality;
- water pollution;
- waste management;
- energy;
- transport, etc.

It then called for an overview and an understanding of how they fitted together. And it said that this was wanted for a maximum specified price of £18,000.

In retrospect, the county council was rather over-optimistic about what could be achieved for £18,000. Either the consultants themselves were also over-optimistic or they were too polite to mention this. At least one consultancy did not tender because they felt that the tender was unworkable, and that they would come in again once this was discovered and the council was forced to re-tender.

Another issue in auditing, then, is whether the price should be stated at the outset, or whether it should be left blank to see what comes up. If it is left blank, the answer that comes up is £200,000–300,000; it's no good going through that exercise if there's not that much money available to spend. With increasing experience in environmental auditing, consultants should be able to gauge better, in a more constructive tender process, what can be expected for a given price.

The county council short-listed three consultants of the 8–10 that were invited to tender, and then spent a day with these consultants. Aspinwalls were appointed in late July 1990, and the contract was signed in time for an autumn start.

Aspinwalls initially said that the audit would take four to six months. They proposed to conduct it in a number of stages: background data collection, preliminary data assessment, site visits, final data assessment, report preparation; and recommendations for future action.

During the first stage of this process, in autumn 1990, they circulated questionnaires to all the departments in the county council, and also outside, to get an understanding of the allocation of responsibilities inside the county council and the sources of information available. Towards the end of the year, they also interviewed a range of contact staff in the various county council departments. This was found to be more time-consuming than had originally been expected. The county council had not realised how much of its own time the data collection would take. Taking the council staff's time into account, the actual cost of the audit was much higher than expected.

By the end of 1990, the consultants had collected a vast quantity of data about the environment in Oxfordshire. But they still identified gaps in that data which needed to be filled and consequently the audit was running behind schedule. To give an idea of the rate of progress, Aspinwalls prepared a preliminary draft report in mid February 1991. The county council spent a large amount of time pointing out areas where the report could be improved or where further information was needed. Again, this took more time than expected. A second version of the draft report came out in March. This time it was also given to the councillors for comment. After further work, the final report was delivered in July 1991.

The audit report contains a number of sections, as listed earlier. Each of these sections contains:

- an introduction;
- a brief statement of what is happening at the moment;
- a longer analysis; and
- key issues and the way forward.

Some sections also discuss opportunities and threats, so each section contains both data and an analysis of what needs to be considered about the future.

It took well over twice as long as originally estimated by the consultants to produce the document. Starting from when the county council originally started to think about the need for an audit, the process took about two years. Only the consultants know how much they actually spent on the study, but it is likely that it cost them far more than the £18,000 they contracted to do it for.

The county council published the audit report in autumn 1991; copies cost £25 for non-commercial organisations and £50 for commercial organisations. Copies of the report were made available in all of Oxfordshire's libraries. More importantly, the council published a summary of the audit which covered key data, and which included a response sheet so that people could write in with their views. Travelling exhibitions on the audit went around the county. This was expected to trigger a period of public consultation in early 1992. Discussions within the county council in mid 1992 will then determine what actions need to be taken and how to prioritise the recommendations put forward in the audit.

CASE STUDY
The National Trust
This case study is based on a talk given by Rob Jarman (1991) of the National Trust

The National Trust is a UK charity established in 1895 which owns approximately 570,000 acres of land. Its purposes include 'the permanent preservation for the benefit of the nation of lands and tenements . . . of natural interest or beauty or historic interest'. The statutory requirement to *permanently preserve* the Trust's assets makes the Trust the only organisation with such a remit; in that context, it should be a lead organisation demonstrating environmentally-sustainable management throughout its policies and practices. This concept was put to the Trust's management in the beginning of 1989. The response was that the Trust should establish two strategies:

1 to assess the likely impacts upon Trust interests of environmental change and to see how the Trust should respond to national and international policy initiatives; and
2 to assess the Trust's own policies and practices for their environmental impact and to make recommendations for change where appropriate.

The second strategy became the Trust's environmental audit. The audit project was set up in early 1990, and an initial list of duties for the audit co-ordinator was produced. The audit was set up as a two-year project with two half-time staff covering the whole of the Trust's interests, the funding being approximately £25,000 per year.

The first hurdle was that of raising staff awareness as to what an Environmental Audit was: the staff's initial reaction was generally to question what the audit actually had to do with them. The first task of the audit was thus to identify the range of activities carried out by the National Trust, by meeting the regional management teams and head office departments, using an initial issues list to catalyse discussion. The issues list included:

- buildings (energy conservation, materials, waste disposal);
- vehicles (both leased and owned by the Trust);
- office management;
- enterprises;
- finances; and
- land management (agriculture, forestry, horticulture/gardens, countryside habitat management).

It was thus possible to look at issues raised and to determine the experience of regional practitioners in managing for those interests.

On the basis of the issues list, staff were asked where they felt that significant environmental impacts were occurring. Some issues were written off as being of little importance, while others were identified as being important to the Trust and therefore as warranting more immediate action. As a result, in October 1990 seven main subject headings were produced:

- waste management;
- transport;

- energy conservation and efficiency in buildings;
- renewable energy;
- agriculture;
- office and property management; and
- environmental considerations in the Trust's structures.

For each subject heading target dates were set by which time results were expected, and responsibility for achieving these targets was assigned to specific individuals.

For instance, for waste management the following tasks were set up:

- prepare guidelines for septic tanks husbandry;
- review problems caused to septic tank systems by catering operations;
- modify sewage management provisions in five-year surveys;
- review potential for waste recycling from properties and produce interim report; and
- conduct a regional survey of sewage discharges and prepare an interim report on management strategy.

After these tasks are fulfiled, further issues or areas for improvement are often identified. For instance, the study on waste recycling identified one site on which employees were sorting aluminium cans from steel cans, both of which were sold on the site, for recycling. A change was implemented whereby only aluminium cans were sold: this resulted in no staff time lost to sorting, and a maximisation of recycling income from the aluminium cans.

Following the two-year pilot project, the Trust in 1992 established a full-time Environmental Audit section within the Chief Agent's Department, employing an EA Advisor and an assistant. This section will advise the Trust on the environmental impact and related management changes of its activities.

PART III

Implementing Environmental Audit: The Corporate Environmental Programme and Total Quality Management

Earlier we considered the business setting (Part I) and procedures in corporate strategy (Part II) which produce corporate environmental programmes. In Part III we consider the detailed specification and management of environmental auditing in corporate environmental programmes, using the guidelines of Total Quality Management. The management of corporate environmental programmes and environmental auditing encompasses the following sequence of operations.

Stage 1   Preparing the corporate setting (Chapter 7)
- Gaining management commitment
- Implementing Total Quality Management in the environmental programme

Stage 2   Carrying out the audit: techniques (Chapter 8)
- Setting objectives
- Contract procedures
- Characterising and identifying impacts
- Assessing impact significance
- Identifying and assessing alternatives
- Reporting
- Verification and validation

Stage 3   Generating strategic advantage   (Chapter 9)
- Environmental strategy as a way of surviving competition
- Environmental companies as change-based and value-driven

- Environmental programmes as emphasising quality
- Total involvement of all personnel
- Commitment to training and communication
- Emphasis on co-operation and incentives, not blame
- Self-realisation in management development and corporate strategy

7 PREPARING THE CORPORATE SETTING FOR EFFECTIVE ENVIRONMENTAL AUDITING

GAINING MANAGEMENT COMMITMENT

Managers at the top work in a harassed and complex setting, and a corporate environmental programme will increase this complexity. For some top managers this constitutes a competitive agenda for their main priorities. It is thus the environmental manager's responsibility to:

- show how the corporate environmental programme will provide positive opportunities for the enterprise;
- define how individual top managers can contribute to and gain from the corporate environmental programme; and
- set up systems for maintaining full management control over the corporate environmental programme, while at the same time sustaining its autonomy and independence. As financial audit has the same problem, this objective is not unfamiliar to the organisation.

Whenever new operations and policies are established in a company, they can be seen as 'innovative products'. Innovation must be sold in competition with other, better-established strategies. Even if external codes and new legal requirements are having an impact on company strategy, board directors may not have had the time or opportunity to become aware of the change or of its resource and investment implications.

Because there are competing issues demanding attention and resources, gaining management commitment to the corporate environmental programme and environmental audit must be seen as a 'marketing' problem. In this sense, marketing consists fundamentally of a communications exercise: information about an essential new product is brought to the attention of buyers and their capacity to act positively is accelerated. Figure 7.1 shows an approach to marketing environmental audit to top management.

Step 1 comprises a *'marketing audit'* of corporate environmental issues. This step involves the preparation and distribution of a brief

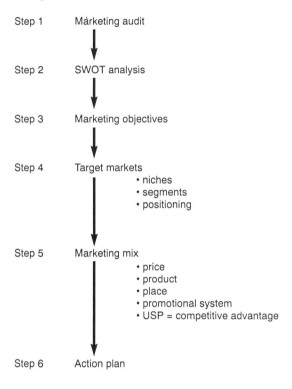

Figure 7.1 *Marketing environmental audit*

questionnaire to top managers. The questionnaire will provide a profile of their understanding of environmental issues and corporate responsibilities. This questionnaire's results can then become the basis for focus panels and one-to-one interviews. The objective is to gain a closer appreciation of top management's perceived priorities in environmental matters and how these are seen as connecting to other corporate priorities.

Step 2 builds a picture of strengths, weaknesses, opportunities and threats (SWOT). SWOT can be used to highlight the potentials for development and the possible legal, financial or marketing problems that may arise as a result of the programme or audit. Figure 7.2 gives an example of SWOT for an audit of a company's waste management policy.

Step 3, fixing *marketing objectives*, allows for this information to be converted into a limited set of internal communications objectives for the

Strengths	Weaknesses
● potential savings ● reduction of paper consumption ● use of waste management to strengthen internal Quality Management systems	● cost of implementing waste management systems without compensating benefits ● increased expectations may be disappointed ● effective implementation requires massive support from management, finance
Opportunities	**Threats**
● sale of waste paper ● potential recycling of material ● improved public environmental image	● half-hearted implementation may destroy public confidence in further measures

Figure 7.2   SWOT analysis in environmental projects: an example of a corporate waste management policy

corporate environmental programme. Briefly, strengths should be emphasised, e.g. the environmental programme assures corporate compliance with new regulatory codes. Weaknesses need to be down-played or offset in some way, e.g. although environmental programmes may erode profit margins, they also assure continued business operations without intervention from authorities. Similarly, threats should be placed in a context which converts them to opportunities, e.g. environmental programmes threaten the long-term proprietary patents of the company, therefore additional new patents should be sought for technologies that have assured environmental viability. Finally, opportunities should be emphasised where environmental programmes connect readily to corporate strategy, e.g. a good understanding of production by-products and waste management can lead to new product families and enhanced corporate income.

Step 4 involves the identification of *target markets* for this exercise, namely those top managers who have an inherent sympathy for, or operational links with, the corporate environmental programme. On any board, and certainly on a main company board, there will be two or three persons in this role. They comprise the specific niche for this product, for their understanding and fluent advocacy of the corporate environmental programme will determine much of its reception within the board's deliberations.

Step 5, *marketing mix*, means shaping, in co-ordination with a good understanding of specific buyers and niche allies, the corporate environmental programme. Its content, costs, positioning within the organisation, and promotion and communications must all be considered against the known preferences and perceptions of top management. Out of this a unique selling proposition (USP) must be created. The USP of a well-designed corporate environmental programme must be such that a majority of the board, and certainly the chief executive officer and chair, will easily become committed not only to its purposes but also its procedures, priorities, form and operational resourcing.

All of these elements are placed within Step 6, an *action plan* for mounting the presentation to the board and its advisers and deputies. Test marketing should also occur at this point: this step can pinpoint flaws and sticking points which can then be amended or downgraded, before the final corporate environmental programme is presented for decision.

Clearly, each of these steps also needs to be taken when major renewals of the programme or its major components are required. Specific projects will require additional work and communications to gain commitment, particularly when they relate to major new investments or potential liabilities on existing plant or products. In this respect, the use of SWOT analysis is again relevant. For each project or strategy, SWOT can be used to highlight the potentials for development and environmental improvements, and to anticipate possible legal, financial, environmental or marketing problems.

This marketing model for the corporate environmental programme is strongly recommended. Environmental managers tend to come from technical backgrounds in science, planning or engineering, where there is relatively little emphasis on customer-led product development. It is assumed that the best technical standard, depending on which institute or university the environmental manager was most recently trained at, will also be the right one to be used in particular organisational settings. However, companies and organisations differ radically, not only in their main businesses, but also in their internal structures, ways of thought and methods of decision-making and product development. Therefore, effective design and implementation of the corporate environmental programme must be focused on adapting good externally validated technical standards to the internal culture and way of work.

This also has the effect of making the environmental manager much more of a 'company man' (regardless of gender). Therefore, the issues of independence and autonomy must also be addressed.

Often the audit will require additional expenditure of time and effort by operational managers. To operational managers who have no previous experience with environmental concerns, the results of the audit usually seem to offer more threats than opportunities. The environmental agenda is both more subjective and less well understood than financial or operational priorities. The auditor must therefore be more than a critic: he or she must be able to motivate the operational manager and indeed establish leadership through persuasion. In this respect, his or her obligations reach beyond that of inspection. The audit must be a joint effort, requiring a balanced interplay of auditee with auditor. Goals, objectives and criteria must be jointly agreed as valid. The auditor must be an active listener and learner along with the operational managers as both are part of the quality assurance management.

TOTAL QUALITY MANAGEMENT IN THE ENVIRONMENTAL PROGRAMME

Procedures for establishing Total Quality Management systems for the corporate environmental programme are complex. These procedures are highly visible to both clients and the staff involved in the corporate operations being environmentally reviewed. There must be a high level of confidence in the process and the personnel involved. It is comparable in this respect to an internal financial audit: the perceived credibility of the process and its implementors determines the acceptability of the final audit. Quality control of the corporate environmental programme is thus at the heart of its credibility: without perceived quality control, the corporate environmental programme has no legitimacy either inside or outside the organisation. For this reason, the systematic application of Total Quality Management to the corporate environmental programme is essential.

Smith and Yodis (1989) note:

> The idea that managing for quality is different from striving to achieve program goals is a seductive, but false, notion. High quality cannot be achieved as a separate endeavour, but must be planned into the program and designed to be attained at the outset.

For a corporate environmental programme, Total Quality Management may be defined as the comprehensive identification and motivation of all parts of the organisation's human and technical resources towards fulfilment of the agreed corporate environmental mission of the organisation. Total Quality Management in this area of corporate development builds on the established quality assurance and management programmes of recent years.

Total Quality Management focuses in particular on training, motivation and increasingly decentralised responsibility for all people in the organisation. Quality is not an externally applied post-operation procedure, but is integrated into every aspect of the work and life of the organisation. Every member, down to the most junior, must take full responsibility for the corporation's environmental objectives. Through training, example and motivation programmes, workers must learn continually to inspect and control their own work, taking action at every stage to ensure that corporate objectives are accurately reflected in their personal area of responsibility.

Environmental outputs of large organisations are diverse and diffuse. They are often controlled by the least senior and most marginalised members of the organisation, who have low pay, minimal training and poor promotion prospects. However, when it is well understood Total Quality Management empowers an organisation's members. It acknowledges that all roles are of equal importance, from the most junior clerical and support staff through to top management. For instance, in hospitals, where its application is under way, roles such as those of cleaning and orderly staff have been 'job enriched'. This has produced increasing job satisfaction and better awareness of quality and service delivery for customers.

Although Total Quality Management cannot change relative pay or seniority, it can be made part of a job enrichment programme. The operatives' tasks and roles must be underscored and management must pay particular attention to them, as their performance will profoundly affect the corporate environmental programme. Any problems of low job-role esteem – that is, feelings of low status and powerlessness – will reflect back on the operatives' refusal to take the waste management or the energy saving agendas, for instance, with appropriate seriousness. On the other hand, a job enrichment programme incorporating the requirements of the corporate environmental programme can in turn lead to much more predictable ongoing environmental management measures.

Carrying out an environmental audit strikes deep at the heart of the organisation and its ambitions in the present business world. Each part of the audit procedure, from the initial framing of terms of reference to the final report and determination of action, can be subjected to severe tests of quality. Each part must be seen as fully rational, appropriate to the organisation and targeted at key environmental issues. For each phase of the audit, a period of careful preparation is required. Full discussion and active communication with operators and neighbours is important.

Following an initial round of information assembly, discussions, shared creative sessions and committee meetings, a period of creative synthesis is essential. A good audit report must do more than contain a series of analyses and recommendations. It must also show how the analyses were carried out, to document the qualitative control of the process. Sources of data and information must be accessibly presented. The research and information process must be seen to have been executed in a vigorous and thoughtful manner. Finally, a comprehensive image of the environmental status of the strategy/product must be developed. Without a highly professional commitment to researching and reporting with full attention to detail, an opportunity to achieve enhanced environmental performance may be lost.

Each step of the corporate environmental programme must have a quality assurance procedure designed into it. Quality checks should be part of the routine presentation of the results of audit programmes. The environmental manager, by definition, is concerned with achieving excellence in the physical and product environment. For that reason, he or she must ensure that the audit procedures being used have been shown to be excellent.

The corporate environmental programme's manager is essentially a quality control manager for that programme. It is essential that, as the corporate environmental programme matures, its managers have full evidence concerning the level of quality and professionalism being delivered by its staff. The corporate environmental programme's manager will focus on maintaining quality in the following areas of the audit:

- process;
- practices;
- resources;
- skills; and
- activities.

A system must be set up which allows staff to execute audits in a consistent and professional manner, and which has built-in systems of communicating those facts to the rest of the organisation. This will include a range of checklists and brief management reports, some of which are listed in Figure 8.6. A method of succinctly summarising the progress and quality of all audit projects within the environmental unit is required; this could take the form of twice-monthly progress summaries, to be reviewed among project managers within the unit. The following reviews need to be carried out on a weekly basis:

- supervision of staff;
- review of programme and project goals;
- review of programme and project resources;
- employee training and performance review, both informal and formal;
- accuracy and clarity of report formats and procedures;
- objectivity of auditors, including independence from auditee organisations and units, and provisions for validation and verification by external agencies where required.

In this respect, the corporate environmental programme manager is in the same position as other corporate managers. He or she must review and refine continuously all aspects of the audit procedure. No system can be regarded as not requiring change. There is no one permanent right or best way to carry out any scientific, managerial or design procedure. All systems must be reviewed periodically, and improvements made systematically and repeatedly. The full commitment of all personnel to the joint task becomes critical, as industry becomes more information-based and less material-based. Value leadership is the prime measure of all managers in the new industrial settings.

Compliance conditioning is a term for the process of moving the whole of the organisation towards quality commitment in the corporate environmental programme. The term 'conditioning' is used in order to underscore the fact that management must use a range of motivators to trigger the adoption and rigorous application of environmental codes to all aspects of the organisation's outputs. This can be done in co-ordination with and alongside other quality management targets: financial, productivity, timekeeping, customer service and satisfaction.

Environmental objectives are a significant new set of quality indicators. Compliance with these objectives requires the acquisition of new skills and attitudes throughout the organisational structure. Thus, a repertory of motivators and penalties, with the accent on rewards, will be a necessary component of the full adoption of a corporate environmental programme.

The different forms of conditioners in the organisation can be arrayed from positive to negative, and voluntary to compulsory: Figure 7.3 gives examples of different forms of conditioners. They can be operated from either inside the organisation or by external regulators and/or stakeholder groups, e.g. Greenpeace. In terms of corporate development, their operation inside the system is far more preferable and cost-effective.

	Negative	*Positive*
Voluntary	– Media exposure of poor environmental practices – Investor and insurer information programmes to publicise environmental non-compliance	– Good practice awards – Voluntary audit certification programmes – Training programmes and certification of skills – Environmental management awards – New facility/operations environmental awards/ certificates

Compulsory	– Penalties
	  – financial
	  – desist orders
	  – operations
	  – curtailment or shutdown
	– Criminal charges
	  – against management
	  – against operatives
		– Audit certification programmes

Figure 7.3   Examples of environmental code compliance conditioners

Finally the corporate environmental programme unit must itself be subject to a quality audit from an outside corporate unit, so that its reputation for quality and performance are consistent with its mission to alter the environmental performance of the corporation.

8 CARRYING OUT THE AUDIT: TECHNIQUES

This chapter reviews techniques for conducting an environmental audit. These include techniques for:

- setting objectives;
- establishing contract procedures;
- characterising and describing impacts;
- assessing the significance of impacts;
- identifying and assessing alternatives;
- considering the need for a more detailed audit;
- reporting; and
- verification and validation.

SETTING OBJECTIVES

Achieving the objectives of an environmental audit will depend on the character of the procedure which is laid out. Objectives must be specified with clarity and precision if they are to be achieved. They must be reachable and measurable. But, more importantly, a method of cascading the requirements of the corporate environmental programme into the whole of large complex organisations unfamiliar with environmental compliance is essential.

Objectives must be considered repeatedly during the planning and contracting phase of the environmental audit. The choice of objectives will be substantially related to the corporate resources available to achieve these objectives. What appears necessary in early stages may be found to be impossible or unnecessary as the understanding of corporate objectives increases. Real problems exist in setting feasible objectives for the environmental audit. Whether the organisation is capable of achieving its stated objectives will be dictated by the availability of resources required: staff, training, knowledge of protocols, details of legislation, availability of advice concerning external compliance and advisory staff.

The understanding of what objectives are feasible must be reached during the planning stage of an audit. The principal means of understanding is through prolonged interviewing of, and monitoring communications from, internal and external actors: senior management, operations managers, enforcement agencies and, where required, local community groups.

CONTRACT PROCEDURES

The initial setting of terms of reference, scope and powers of environmental audit is a critical stage. The contract can be within the organisation or with outside contractors. Where outside contractors are involved in a competitive tender procedure, there must be explicit definitions of relevant quality controls. This will allow for bids that reflect the full range of costs that are liable to be incurred. Where the audit will be carried out internally, it is equally important that the early 'contract' stage, specifying the scope and obligations of the audit team and procedures, costs and responsibilities, be well detailed.

The following circumstances require particularly careful tendering and contracting procedures, because of the potential financial and/or legal liabilities that may be incurred, depending on the findings of the audit:

- disposal of a major facility or property;
- acquisition of a major facility or property;
- valuation of a major facility or property;
- class legal actions in regard to pollution and contamination from specific sites or manufacturing procedures; and
- government regulatory compliance.

The contract or tender specification must detail at each step of the audit:

- quality checks to be used;
- detailed protocols to be employed;
- publication of raw and analysed data;
- report drafting and review;
- right of the client to vet the final drafting; and
- control over publication and dispersal findings.

Where legal considerations are paramount, data may be deposited with a custodian, usually a well-established law firm, who will ensure that they are not tampered with and that accurate information is analysed and used in the final report. Figure 8.1 sets out the contents of a proposed contract for an environmental audit.

CHARACTERISING AND DESCRIBING IMPACTS

Impacts must be characterised and described to help decision-makers understand their relative importance for the environment and for corporate policy, product feasibility or plant operations. Impacts can broadly be described as:

Direct or	Indirect
Intended	Accidental
Positive	Negative
Immediate	Longer-term
Discrete	Cumulative
Quantitative	Qualitative

Impacts can also be described by their nature, direction, location and magnitude.

Many different lists exist of what impacts should be considered during environmental assessment or auditing. A number of these are included in Appendix B. The proposed EC Eco-Audit Directive considers:

- data on energy and material exchanges between industry and environment;
- compliance with applicable regulations and standards;
- significant incidents or operation disturbance and resulting complaints;
- review of available policy, equipment, organisation and management systems concerning
  - pollution discharge control and other nuisance,
  - energy choice, reduction of energy use,
  - choice of raw materials,
  - reduction in use of waste and raw materials,
  - transport, elimination, recycling and reuse of waste,
  - product planning (design, packaging, transport, use, elimination),
  - prevention and mitigation of accidents,
  - staff training and participation,
  - external information, and
  - method of transport.

1 Written audit plan, including:
   - subjects of audit
   - audit strategies to be used
   - numbers and qualifications of auditors
   - duration of audit
   - time frame and specified reporting dates

2 Agreement on structure and custody of final report. Agreement on format of final report, with specimen of non-commercial report to show approach

3 Agreement on peer review of auditors, requiring working papers and draft report to be reviewed by a qualified external auditor not involved in the contract

4 Right of review and, if acceptable, right to modify draft report by client and representatives

5 Right of review of draft report by legal counsel and/or corporate solicitor. If the potential obligations – legal, financial, corporate – are substantial, arrange for the solicitor/counsel to be the repository of all correspondence. If this is required, the legal firm should be involved at the contract stage

6 Agreement on limits and areas in which the environmental auditor will make recommendations and otherwise obligate the corporation. The scope of the audit may restrict the report to a display of information only, with only a preliminary interpretation and no recommendations. This must be specified

7 Agreement on scientific protocols, the collection and analysis of field data, and specification of the qualified scientific laboratory to be used. If data analysis is critical, protocols for analysis should be specified at the contract stage. This specification may reflect the need for such procedures as duplicate and/or split samples

8 Review of specific auditors to be assigned to the job. Assess the strengths and weaknesses of the team as a whole, on the basis that an adequate audit is always a team effort. No one person has the requisite range of skills and expertise fully to comprehend the environmental impact of a major facility or large property development

9 Interview the team leader (not his or her senior director, or junior associate), to ensure that you are confident in the personal qualities of this key member

10 Agree on a general plan for any difficulties which may arise during the audit. Develop contractual procedures for unforeseen contingencies, such as:
   - lack of availability of, e.g. key staff, key laboratories etc.
   - unscheduled plant shutdowns
   - unforeseen discoveries and disclosures

Figure 8.1   Proposed contents of a contract for an environmental audit

(adapted from S. D. Hoffman, 'Planning, Staffing and Contracting for an Environmental Audit', in Smith and Yodis, 1989)

MATRIX ANALYSIS OF INFORMATION

A simple and commonly-used technique for identifying and summarising the environmental impacts of a strategy/product is the preparation of an interaction matrix. Such a matrix lists environmental components along the vertical axis and the components of the project or policy along the horizontal axis. The impact of the project/policy component on the environmental component is then marked in the appropriate matrix cell (see Leopold et al, 1971).

Figure 8.2 shows part of a simple interaction matrix for a hypothetical operation. If a project component affects the environmental component – for instance if the use of the road affects air quality – a checkmark is placed in the appropriate cell. Figure 8.3 shows a more complex matrix, where impacts are not only identified, but also described as positive or negative, large or small.

A further refinement is shown at Figure 8.4, where each cell contains two numbers. The number at the top left denotes the impact's magnitude, from $+10$ (very positive) to -10 (very negative), with 0 as no impact or a

	Construction		Operation	
	Project	Road	Project	Road
Human beings	×		×	×
Flora	×	×	×	
Fauna	×	×	×	×
Soil	×			
Water	×			
Air				×
Climate				
Landscape	×			
Interactions			×	×
Material assets			×	
Cultural heritage	×	×	×	×

Figure 8.2   Environmental Impact Identification Matrix: Simple

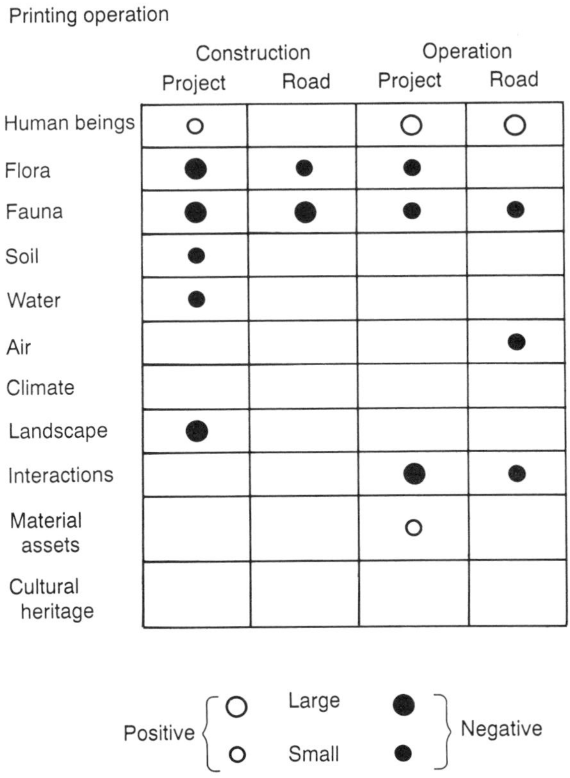

Printing operation

| | Construction | | Operation | |
	Project	Road	Project	Road
Human beings	○		○	○
Flora	●	●	●	
Fauna	●	●	●	●
Soil	●			
Water	●			
Air				●
Climate				
Landscape	●			
Interactions			●	●
Material assets			○	
Cultural heritage				

Positive { ○ Large ● } Negative
         { ○ Small ● }

Figure 8.3 Environmental impact identification matrix: magnitude analysis

neutral impact. The number at the bottom right denotes the impact's significance, from 0 (no significance) to 10 (very significant).

This dual scale acknowledges the fact that an impact may be large but insignificant, or small but significant. For example, a policy requiring office paper to be recycled may have a large positive impact on waste disposal, but may be of only limited significance if the market is already saturated with paper to be recycled. On the other hand, the disposal of even small amounts of certain chemicals (eg. heavy metals or CFCs) may have a significant impact on the receiving environment.

Interaction matrices obviously have limitations. They must be carefully designed to be effective: the definition of the project/policy components must be done carefully and all pertinent environmental components must be listed. The decision of whether an impact is large or small, significant

Impact identification:
modified Leopold matrix

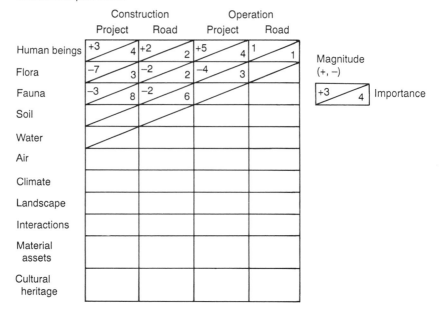

Figure 8.4 Environmental impact identification matrix: magnitude/significance analysis

(adapted from Leopold et al., 1971)

or insignificant, is also subject to interpretation: a sociologist could be expected to find social impacts more important than an ecologist would; and an environmental expert may give different importance weightings than a local landowner.

Different matrices could be prepared for different scenarios, eg. for different mitigation measures, alternative locations or different work practices. The temptation to add up or average various parts of the matrix, or directly to compare matrices should, however, be avoided. Some impact identification techniques attempt to give importance weightings to the impacts and then directly compare them, but the weightings are subject to interpretation and tend to foster debate rather than quell it.

Matrices help to ensure that all impacts are considered in an environmental audit. They summarise information concisely and clearly: looking across rows, one can see the total impacts on a component of the environment, and looking down columns one can see the total impact of individual project components. This can suggest mitigation measures which could minimise environmental harm or maximise environmental benefits. The use of matrices in audit presentation can also help to clarify what assumptions have been made during the audit, and provide a clear framework for decision-making.

ASSESSING THE SIGNIFICANCE OF IMPACTS

All operations involve many tradeoffs. Traditionally, environmental objectives have been sacrificed to economic, social and commercial objectives. Environmental auditing now requires that such choices be made explicit, and places limits on the degree and number of environmental sacrifices which are tolerable. The whole purpose of audit concerns the redefinition of environmental impacts from the area of the trivial into that of the significant. Yet in practice there are limits: over the years, various countries' environmental regulations have recognised these limits with such legal definitions as 'Best Available Techniques Not Entailing Excessive Cost' (BATNEEC), 'Best Practicable Environmental Option' (BPEO), and other clauses which 'harmonise' economic and environmental imperatives.

In many cases the best decision that can be achieved is a general determination of the environmental significance of strategic or operational impacts. The limits of both research budgets and scientific procedures also make it likely that this can only be achieved for individual issues or factors, rather than for collective and interactive impacts on the environment.

The audit must thus focus on issues which are agreed to be relevant and non-trivial by decision-makers and their advisers. This involves placing greatest emphasis on the more important impacts and linkages, especially those for which there may be some choice and flexibility in operations or design. The object is to provide not the greatest possible amount of information, but rather the most essential information.

When determining the significance of impacts the auditor must consider that:

- assessment of significance calls for a balanced consideration of technical factors as well as social values;
- concerns and priorities may vary considerably from one stakeholder group to another; and

- many environmental impacts are complex, with a mixture of positive and negative aspects. Some of these will be more critical than others.

Assessment of significance involves drawing a generalised conclusion regarding the net environmental effects and their consequences.

The significance of an environmental effect and its consequences can be assessed in relation to each of a number of characteristics. There is no objective scale to measure the significance of an impact with regard to any of these characteristics; nor is there a meaningful weighting index to calculate their combined impact or the significance of the net environmental results of a strategy, product or operation. Issues of significance in audit are thus at least as much a reflection of subjective values as of objective criteria. Even with a high degree of consensus on the acceptability of specific effects and consequences, there is typically no magic threshold at which effects and consequences change from 'insignificant' to 'significant': it is usually a question of degree. An assessment of significance can thus only be based on good judgement and experience.

For this reason, the distinction between environmental thresholds and thresholds of significance must be clearly maintained. An environmental threshold is the point at which some environmental impact dramatically shifts in form or magnitude, e.g. as a function of some physical or biochemical process. A threshold of significance implies some evaluative judgements of the importance or significance of an impact. There are no practical units of measure that can meaningfully depict the precise degree of significance of any environmental impact.

IDENTIFYING AND ASSESSING ALTERNATIVES

Environmental auditing is a dynamic and iterative process, where major policy alternatives and/or minor variations thereof are continually explored and assessed. Ideally, the broad options are defined in the policy formulation stage before the audit is begun, but the door should always be open to new ideas and approaches that may be discovered in the audit stage itself.

Alternatives can include mitigatory, ameliorative and compensatory options that can help to minimise or offset anticipated negative impacts, or enhance achievement of positive impacts. Monitoring and follow-up are also needed. However, the determination of possible mitigation measures should be a last resort to deal with anticipated negative environmental impacts, or insufficient achievement of positive environmental objectives. The first priority should be to identify potentially acceptable alternatives that can prevent negative effects, or which actively promote positive environmental benefits. Only when all viable and acceptable options have been tested, should attention turn to identifying mitigatory measures.

An option appraisal matrix is a simple way of identifying and measuring alternatives, and an example is shown in Figure 8.5. The objective of this step cannot be a detailed description of all possible options. Rather, the analysis should focus on the most relevant options

Task: In the setting of a large business, to identify the most effective method of reducing waste paper that is not recycled

	Option A	**B**	**C**
	Hire external wastepaper collector	Set up internal wastepaper system	Do nothing
Sub-objectives			
● Minimise cost	−4	+3	+1
● Maximise revenue	+2	+3	−3
● Minimise work disruption	+1	+4	+4
● Reduce net waste to 25% of present figure in 60 months	+4	+2	−10
● Optimise total energy budget	0	0	−4
Scoring totals:	+3	+12	−14

Figure 8.5   Option appraisal matrix
Example of an application to a corporate environmental programme

that best portray meaningful choices for the decision-makers' consideration.

CONSIDERING THE NEED FOR MORE DETAILED AUDIT

The environmental audit is an iterative procedure. That is, the quality of its findings improve with multiple, increasingly refined repetitions of its procedures and data analysis. In this key respect, an environmental audit differs from a financial audit. It consists of not arriving at a single best answer, but instead of approximating over time a series of increasingly more accurate data and better environmental practices. The volume and level of detail of information provided should be sufficient for fully-informed decision-making, without being excessive.

Preliminary screening and assessment can serve to define issues and select methods for more detailed assessment. The preliminary audit may tend to rely on relatively standardised techniques. The detailed audit, instead, may require considerable adaptation of approaches to deal with particular challenges such as:

- technical complexity;
- unique data sources;
- specialist consultations required; and
- expensive field surveys to execute.

Figure 8.6 contrasts the main differences in methods between a preliminary and a detailed audit. It should be remembered that the audit procedure may need to be repeated a number of times, each time with increasing refinement and tighter scoping. Any given iteration may have characteristics of both preliminary and detailed levels.

Detailed audit is not warranted where:

- the preliminary audit reveals no appreciable environmental effects;
- only modest potential effects are revealed, and more detailed analysis will not significantly enhance understanding of their nature or alter their weighting;
- the preliminary audit reveals major environmental impacts, but further analysis is not justified because the analysis from the preliminary audit is already seen as adequately detailed and rich;
- technical limitations prevent a detailed audit from being undertaken,

	Preliminary audit	Detailed audit – in addition to items for preliminary audit
Sources of information	Published, existing data are used	Requires original data collection
Means of data gathering	Desk research, data banks, on-line searches, expert consultation	Field research, laboratory analysis
Techniques	Analysis of similar cases; use of published data and standards	Simulations (laboratory, field); pilot studies; comparative analyses of similar cases
Reliability expectations	Expected to be reasonable within corporate requirements	Expected to be rigorous and sustainable against external scientific and legal examination
Risk assessment	Judged not to be critical	Judged as critical to public or safety and health
Costs, resources, timing	Minimal, quick	May be considerable; extended period
Use of experts	Brief consultation	Extensive involvement
Peer review	Usually none	Important validation component
Team structure	Internal team	Expert team, using external resources
Stakeholder consultation	Minimal	Extensive

Figure 8.6   Contrasts between preliminary and detailed audit procedures

e.g. insufficient information is available, scientific models are inadequate, reliable data are unobtainable.

Conversely, detailed audit is warranted where:

- there is reason to believe that the preliminary audit was insufficiently detailed to support decisions;
- impacts identified in the preliminary audit are so substantial as to justify additional research;
- in some other respect, understanding of impacts will enhance the quality of the design or other decisions.

REPORTING

The outcome of the environmental audit can be communicated both in an audit report, and through meetings and live briefings. The audit report may be in several volumes, with a single summary report pulling together the main findings for general circulation.

The identification of the audiences for various versions of the audit report, as well as technical appendices, is an important and sensitive issue. There are threats and opportunities relating to all the different audiences. The use of SWOT analysis to consider options and test implications of different audiences' reactions can be helpful.

For audiences outside the organisation, there are usually explicit decisions already built into the original decision to carry out the environmental audit. Directors will have clear views as to which 'stakeholders' should receive which materials. Where there is a code compliance objective, the design of the package of material to be submitted for scrutiny is a top-level management decision. It is the task of the environmental unit to facilitate this decision, by showing various options, and costs and benefits attributable to them.

Different audiences, each with different experiences and expertise, will naturally interpret the report in varying ways. A live presentation provides an opportunity to highlight particularly significant findings, address outstanding questions, correct any misinterpretations and provide supplementary information if required.

Such a presentation has several objectives:

- to explain, and ensure the proper interpretation of the observations, findings and recommendations of the report;
- to assist interested parties in understanding the corporate and community implications of the report, and in translating these implications into possible strategy and operations alterations; and
- to foster a mutual understanding and respect between producers and consumers of the report by building a better appreciation of different concerns, perspectives, needs and difficulties in research. This process will enhance future environmental audits.

Many decision-makers are not used to receiving live briefings on audit reports and may not actively seek them. Accordingly, those responsible for the audit may need to be proactive in arranging appropriate presentations before the final decisions are made.

Some of the methods for ensuring active presentation include:

- internal memoranda previewing publication of the report;
- well-publicised private briefings for invited audiences, with internal circulation of the list of those invited;
- direct informal approaches to top management/political leaders and their advisers in order to ensure that they are aware of the arrival of the report and related presentations.

Thus the environmental manager can involve him or herself in the internal politics of the organisation. It is obvious that such steps need to be taken with great care to minimise unnecessary interpersonal friction, so that the overall reception of the audit report is enhanced, rather than otherwise.

Similarly, presentations need not be restricted to final conclusions and recommendations. It may be appropriate to provide decision-makers and stakeholders with interim presentations and/or progress reports, highlighting preliminary findings and tentative recommendations. The manager may wish to seek feedback on key issues which can help identify errors and oversights, and anticipate reaction to the final report, including areas of possible misinterpretation.

VERIFICATION OF AUDIT QUALITY

The quality of the environmental audit is a key issue, because of the potential concern of external stakeholders and activists in corporate environmental performance. Two major areas for sustaining quality need to be developed:

- internal organisational development committed to autonomy – including an autonomous environmental unit – as part of its mission; and
- external verification of the environmental performance and quality of the corporate environmental programme.

Sustaining autonomy

Internal corroboration of environmental performance and quality measurement of the corporate environmental programme is carried out through a variety of techniques and sub-programmes:

- annual and quarterly environmental performance reports;
- sectoral and interorganisational comparative studies;
- peer review procedures;
- five-year summaries of annual environmental performance reports; and
- published plans for environmental performance improvement programmes, including amelioration, mitigation and compensation.

Once established, the environmental audit process must not be seen as potentially displacing the normal corporate or political decision-making power which resides in specified legally responsible groups. The auditors' function is not to determine whether certain options concerning design and mitigation, compensation or amelioration are acceptable; their task is to carry out research and give a reasonably comprehensive appraisal of different options. It is in this sense that the audit sustains its independence and autonomy.

Within this autonomous setting, environmental audit is particularly useful when it helps place technical factors into some useful perspective: e.g. the ecological significance of identified environmental impacts; the technical feasibility of potential mitigatory measures; the economic repercussions of specific impacts. Audit is also powerful when it synthesises the values, priorities and concerns of a number of key stakeholder groups in ways which assist decision-makers to appreciate implications and tradeoffs of various options.

External verification

The final stage in the formal procedure of quality management of environmental audit is the review of its key documents by an external authority.

This may be required by regulation or may be undertaken as part of a voluntary industry-association code, with industry-appointed inspectorates involved. In many countries, a verification authority is being established, relating to the International Standard on Quality Control. In the USA, where substantial growth in environmental auditing has occurred in recent years, different industries have agreed the qualifications for external audit verifiers. In the UK, the Institute of Environmental Assessment has established criteria for the certification of auditors. As environmental audits become more widely required for various industries, verification will become more interlinked with enforcement.

The verification procedure entails a scrutiny of documents relating to the audit, plus relevant supporting technical data. In some cases, interviews may be conducted with company officials to elucidate specific points. Usually the verifier will sample a particular analysis within the audit, to confirm that a randomly chosen component of the audit conforms to acceptable practice. In the case of a major audit, with important investment or enforcement implications, the verifier may visit a site and ask for a particular data protocol to be repeated. If results are parallel to those reported, there is further indication of the overall quality of the work.

But the primary determinant in the verification of the audit report will be that which pertains in the review of any document: it must be coherent, internally consistent and intelligible to the non-expert, while also being fully credible to the expert. Presentation issues always affect credibility, for the readability of a document will enable its findings to be lucidly conveyed to the verifier. For these reasons, as well as those which pertain to good marketing of high-quality products, the greatest care should be taken to present technical documents in the corporate environmental programme which can be exposed to wide publication and scrutiny without apology. Without seeking superficial gloss, the reports must be satisfying as to their professionalism.

9 GENERATING STRATEGIC ADVANTAGE WITH THE CORPORATE ENVIRONMENTAL PROGRAMME

This book has focused on the internal development of corporate culture and quality management, and the relationship of environmental programmes to these areas. This last chapter considers some of the images of corporate change and development currently in use, and how these influence the integration of environmental policy into strategy. Finally, it interlinks the concept of Total Quality Management with strategic competitive concepts.

ENVIRONMENTAL STRATEGY AS A WAY OF SURVIVING INTENSE COMPETITION

Many companies and organisations implementing environmental programmes revel in stable marketplaces, with secure products and, particularly in Europe, quasi-monopoly positions. However, a significant number of export-led companies must survive in less secure marketplaces. Their capacity to adapt to international competition, particularly in the severe recession of the early 1990s, will pivot one way or another on their corporate environmental programmes.

Fast-moving markets in consumer goods respond to environmentally-oriented products, as was seen in the example of Reckitt and Colman's household cleaners (Chapter 2). Cars, too, will increasingly become 'environmentalised', through both legislation and consumer preference. Thus, fast-moving consumer goods companies will show a strong preference for environmentally-led product development strategies over the next decade, as a way of adapting to intensifying competition. In the coming decade, as in recent years, intense competition will involve the rapid invasion and takeover of safe domestic markets by better designed and/or better-value imported products, either from within the local region or from producers in burgeoning developing countries.

'Environmentalisation' has become a major strategy for local companies to continue to hold their home markets. A unique selling proposition will involve not only 'local jobs and local prosperity', but also the cleaning up of plant and product by local producers. If a company takes an ethical stance towards its products, this strategy will form part of the perceived core attraction for increasingly sophisticated consumers.

For instance, in the 1970s and 1980s American cars continued to lose market shares not only because they had less appeal than their Japanese and European competitors, but also because they came from polluting and obsolete factories which were led by corporate bosses publicly obsessed by their 'rights' to national car markets of the 1950s. By becoming environmentalised and well designed, American cars will by the early years of the next century, reclaim their home markets, as is already occurring in Germany and France.

CHARACTERISTICS OF THE ENVIRONMENTALLY-ORIENTED ORGANISATION

Environmental issues will remain part of the market setting for the foreseeable future, as a way of sustaining true customer focus. The organisations best able to take on these environmental issues will be value-driven and change-based; yet they will retain a set of core competencies and an emphasis on quality which will enable them to keep their competitive advantage and remain distinct from other, similar organisations. They will have a strong commitment to training, communication and the empowerment of their workforces, and will emphasise positive actions rather than punishing negative ones.

Value-driven and change-based

The strategic corporations of coming years will be fast changing and boundary-less. These change-based corporations will be able to shift from product-driven to customer-led product strategies within their environmental framework. Living with ambiguity, paradox and the chaos of continuing global change, they will be skilled in reconciling opposites. 'Zen and the art of corporate strategy building' will become a common motto, for Zen, with its seeming contradictions and multi-layered joke meanings, has the spirit of the new age of change which will have to be acquired.

These chameleon companies will emphasise co-ordination and strategic control, for one of their main competencies will lie in this area. Strategic alliances will be found to be essential for a successful environmental performance. Change-based and adaptive, the new networked organisations of the turn of the next century will see their environmental programme as part of a grand alliance, rather than a fortress. The sharing of experience across industry boards and within sectors will provide the principal means of ensuring positive environmental outcomes. Successful businesses will be open to their critics and their competitors on a mutual access basis. As good citizens within their sectors and their communities, the 'environmentalised' corporations will have the security to bare their mistakes and share their environmental learning processes.

Time-based competition will also become part of the environmental programme. Where a cleanup process is under way, as major multinational chemical companies like Dow already demonstrate, continuing competitive advantage can be sustained by showing that progress is under way. The direction of change, the admission of shortcomings and the implementation of remedial strategies are more important in terms of maintaining a customer base than demonstrations of pristine environmental conditions. In any case, claims of purity arouse a degree of scepticism among stakeholder audiences.

Core competencies and an emphasis on quality

Like a human individual, corporate life naturally oscillates between strategic aggressiveness, and the maintenance and sustenance of internal and external relationships. As *Business International* (1992) suggests:

> . . . the traditional model of a company is of an autonomous citadel full of knowledge, capital and skills in a stable world where such attributes are at a premium . . . In today's world, however, knowledge, including technology and capital, are widely available, as are most skills. In addition, markets are becoming ephemeral and liable to sudden change. So it is not merely uneconomic, but dangerous for a company to try to do everything itself.
> (As quoted in *Financial Times* article by Lorenz, 1992)

Lorenz, a leading business journalist adds:

> Companies must themselves learn to become ephemeral, to exploit *ad hoc* alliances of knowledge, skills and capacity . . . [But] this does not mean that

companies must 'abandon fixed emplacements' and 'leave behind their skills of defence'. If they did so entirely, they would have nothing left to bargain and collaborate with. They would be empty shells (*Financial Times*, 1992).[1]

The environmentally-oriented corporations of the future will have to learn to balance collaboration with the important idea of 'core competencies'.[2] Companies must redefine what is their central driving force: for Honda, it is engine technology; for 3m, it is adhesives, coatings and substrates; for Reckitt and Colman, it is domestic purity and cleanliness. Within the environmental field each of these strategic dimensions will take on additional attributes to embrace the corporate environmental programme.

The concept of core competencies relates directly to that of quality. In the famous phrase of Edward Deming, father of the quality movement, a focus on quality means 'delighting the customer'. Companies which focus on their core competencies naturally produce a quality outcome.[3]

The environmental agenda, in the form of new legislation and developing consumer preferences, fits with these traditions. The pursuit of quality in corporate environmental programmes will be easily understood and adopted by the management of many established companies in the advanced industrial world. Rather than constraining corporate goals, it will be seen as liberating management towards higher forms of business development.

All quality management systems have in common a concern for the smallest aspects of product output. Medieval craftsmen working on Gothic cathedrals were told: 'God is in the details', and so it is with the environmental management of large organisations. Getting the fine nuances of energy management, waste treatment, air quality and product design environmentally correct requires sustained attention to the behaviour of the most junior operative, as well as the structure of corporate policy and programme design.

This aim of quality development is increasingly deployed by successful businesses. The Body Shop brings to its customers multi-faceted reassurance about their own priorities – for healthful bodies, benign environments, and ethical business practices. Simultaneously it shows how a huge customer base can be persuaded to pay a high premium for products costing relatively little to produce. Customers at the Body Shop are delighted because they obtain a range of satisfactions in return for their custom. In business jargon, environmentally programmed products at Body Shop increase customers' perceptions of added-value by a greater margin over competing product lines and their companies. As a result, owners, shareholders and ethical investment fund managers are also delighted with the returns on their investment.

Total involvement of all personnel

Because quality management – be it the management of a company's product or of its environmental impacts – concerns attention to details, its practices reach into the whole culture of the business. Good environmental programmes involve the bottom rungs of the organisation; as a result, people trained to implement good environmental procedures at these levels feel more involved in the corporate mission. By contributing to better environmental practices, they can connect their cycle of responsibilities to the company's overall aims.

Peoples' roles in any organisation, from managing director to temporary plant operative, vary enormously in pay and power. Yet, for the purposes of environmental performance all employees occupy equally important positions. For instance, a temporary employee can by mistake release toxic by-products into external water courses. If this is detected, the company's environmental programme of the company will be seen to be inadequate, no matter how carefully the corporate environmental mission has been drafted. Substantial fines and civil damages can result from poor training of site operatives.

A *post-facto* analysis of recent major industrial environmental disasters has shown that the behaviour of people at relatively junior levels in the organisation has triggered major consequences for all of the organisation's employees and stakeholders. The case study of Union Carbide given in Chapter 2 is an example of this.

Another example is the break-up of the Exxon Valdez oil tanker in Alaska through a series of mistakes in training and expectations at several levels of the organisation of the oil giant Exxon. Failures in communications and performance in many operations – ship maintenance, leadership training, enforcement of shipboard duties, training in spillage prevention etc. – resulted in the environmental disaster of a large oil spill on the fragile ocean ecology. As a consequence, five years after the event, financial and legal penalties continue to consume corporate resources which could have been better used in forward planning and prevention of environmental damage. And all these problems still arise some 25 years after the first major oil spill, the break-up of the Torrey Canyon in the English Channel.

The willingness of governments to penalise and legislate has accelerated during this period. Expressions of regret and token payments will not suffice in coming years. Major polluters in industries with a history of environmental damage will increasingly have to value their employees' status equally, controlling both environmental technology and employee training comprehensively, to ensure good environmental performance.

The value-driven network organisations which can best sustain this focus will be brought about by emphasising team-based flat hierarchies with few middle management levels. Thus, the environmentally-oriented corporations of the future will have dismantled much of their corporate hierarchy in order to be flat and fast. These types of organisations will share a common mission, part of which is in the production and development of ethical environmental products.

Commitment to training and communication

The focus on quality in environmental management necessarily leads to important training gains for operatives and managers throughout the organisation. These gains occur because of the concentration on detailed procedures.

A typical focus of environmentally-oriented organisations will be an emphasis on bringing all members of staff 'up to speed'. The development of an awareness of environmental quality, in terms of such issues as energy saving, waste recycling and the reduction of production waste, will rest on a cascading down of good practice from top to bottom. Total involvement means that considerable resources will be placed into training and communication.

Training for better environmental performance will be adopted at each level, and appropriate forms of training will be developed for specific areas of responsibility. Senior managers will need to learn how to evaluate change for its environmental impacts, as well as for its logistical and financial attractiveness. Middle managers will need to acquire an understanding of how their daily routines can be evolved to improve environmental performance. Supervisory managers, the sharp end of the organisation, will often have the greatest potential to produce environmental benefits by properly training their teams in good environmental practices. Finally, operatives will be given, directly through their supervisors and in the overall communications of the organisations, the technology, management systems, incentives and skills for looking after energy and waste management practices. Where product delivery is their responsibility, the environmental dimension will be seen as a further quality issue on which they can be motivated to deliver. Like all total quality strategies, Total Quality Management in environmental practice involves every member of the organisation.

Good environmental management will also require a comprehensive internal approach to communication and decision-making. Operational groups will need to trust specialist contributions from central staff. Environmental managers, in turn, will be required to rely wholly on the enthusiasm of plant supervisors. The open sharing of environmental goals and problems as they arise, between departments, will be essential if code compliance is to be gained.

Communication for a quality-driven environmental programme will focus both on internal and external audiences. The environmentally-oriented corporation will use newsletters, awards and recognition of good practice in environmental performance programmes, alongside quality objectives in other areas of corporate development. The reporting system is crucial here. If teams are to produce environmental improvements, they must know that their successes will be reported upwards in the structure. Significant improvements will need to be given company-wide recognition in this, as in other areas.

For external audiences, news of environmental success, even where present and recent practice has been inadequate, will instil confidence. In some cases, however, environmental performance statistics can adversely affect the business's commercial interests if they are obtained by external critics, business rivals and the media: they will thus need to be deployed with appropriate care, balancing commercial discretion with the business's management development objectives.

These corporate environmental training and communication programmes will lead to direct improvements in both managers and management practices. While imposing real costs, the programmes will provide benefits beyond compliance with environmental codes and image-building.

Emphasis on co-operation and incentives, not blame

Departmental barriers will break down most easily where the skills of environmental managers are focused on supporting, rather than policing, other departments' managers. An atmosphere of mutual trust is easier to describe than to bring about. There are natural rivalries in any organisation, because of inequalities in tasks and resources. For these reasons, the good environmental manager will be people-oriented – sensitive to the needs of others and skillful at finding ways to focus those needs in the delivery of environmental successes for the company.

Operational managers and environmental managers will need to learn how to work together in teams. Each member of the team has a different role: together they will share the responsibility for improving environmental performance, for instance of a facility that has pollution problems, or of a product where sourcing or by-products give rise to undesirable environmental impacts. In management development terms, the ideal approach will be one in which the environmental manager fuses his or her environmental programme with the needs of operational managers to gain additional recognition and resources for operational programmes. There are considerable corporate advantages in having this dual responsibility. By making environmental managers co-responsible for operational issues of various divisions, the company can comply with its environmental goals and improve its business performance simultaneously.

Environmental quality standards and behaviour will be cascaded throughout the organisation – laterally and vertically – and individuals and their team leaders must be given specific missions to produce environmental results, along with other performance criteria. At the operational level, supervisory managers will train their staff to operate as responsible self-managed teams. Within the Total Quality Management perspective, the teams will co-operate in allocating jobs, and in setting tasks and targets. This orientation is essential for environmental performance: each worker is empowered; each team is responsible for itself. Similarly, in white-collar organisations, individuals will be motivated and empowered to improve company performance in areas such as the recycling of waste paper and energy conservation.

One of the several competencies which will be required from managers whose activities affect environmental performance is the capacity to understand and put into action simple procedures for measuring environmental performance over time.

This approach can best be explained by examples. Where liquid outflows from a process plant could potentially lead to unacceptable levels of pollutants, the design of the plant will need to incorporate machinery and procedures for testing the waste water for levels of contaminants. The site managers will need to understand why these samples are taken and the methods by which they are analysed. The resulting numerical measures will need to be generally available and discussed within the site management team. Targets for improvement – i.e. even lower contaminant levels – will need to be agreed, where they are feasible through improved process management.

Similarly, in an office environment with substantial heating and lighting costs, all employees will need to be made aware of the size of the quarterly bills for electricity and other energy. Minor modifications in employee behaviour – closing windows, turning off lights, lowering thermostats, shutting off unnecessary air conditioning – can have substantial benefits in terms of both financial costs and environmental performance. Improved performance targets for energy conservation will be routinely advertised. Day-to-day communications through noticeboards and newsletters will be used to keep awareness of good practices high. Where large goals are aimed at, team awards could be developed. Employee awareness of statistical controls shows how minor changes in attitude and behaviour can affect key measures.

In general, senior management will need to learn to ask more from their managers and operatives. Where statistics about environmental performance need to be spread through the organisation, employees will be asked to educate one another in their significance and meaning.

Environmental programmes will be best put into effect by a system of incentives and rewards, rather than by detection of error and penalties. In practice this means that internal environmental audits should be training oriented, rather than intensively focused on fault-finding and assigning blame. Any errors detected in environmental management will thus become 'training opportunities'.

Failures in achieving targets will not be tied to blame. Instead, the emphasis will be on target review and operations reworking, to ensure that attainable goals are being set and the means to achieving them being made available. Again this will reinforce the message of Total Quality Management. All involved in the company will be jointly engaged in environmental success, which is directly identified as part of the organisation's success.

These prescriptions will liberate the management and workforce of the environmentally-oriented company in many ways. Making a living and becoming richer will become merged with an inner psychological confidence which leads to that highest form of management development, self-realisation.

SELF-REALISATION IN ENVIRONMENTAL MANAGEMENT DEVELOPMENT AND CORPORATE STRATEGY

Self-realisation in management development theory is based on the research of the psychologist Abram Maslow, whose approach to human development has been used to account for the evolving needs of managers and of corporate strategy. In his seminal work of the 1950s, Maslow suggested that human beings progress through a succession, or hierarchy, of needs, which he described as a pyramid:
Figure 9.1 summarises this hierarchy.

Maslow proposes that, at least in the West, these are successive levels of need identification rising from survival needs through to spiritual self-transcendance. In the range of world cultures, however, there are clearly other priorities. For instance, Hindus in traditional South Asian communities may from early life focus on selfless spiritual concerns, without any personal concern for survival. In the West, minority communities, such as the monastics, have also practised selflessness. Their existence indicates that this ordering is culture-bound (Maslow, 1954).

While Maslow is well known in the teaching of human resources development, his images are seldom applied in the area of corporate strategy. However, Maslow's theory has implications for corporate development and its relationship to environmental policy. Once successful business leaders and their organisations have made their organisations secure and profitable in proven markets, they tend to advance to new goals. Founders and managers – and, through them, other organisations – may seek higher levels of social acceptance; and having attained appropriate recognition, they will seek to affect political decisions. Finally, they may aim to make a spiritual contribution to the evolution of their communities.

A few cases may serve to show the usefulness of this notion. Among the most successful UK companies in recent years has been the pharmaceutical company Wellcome Foundation. Originally it was an enterprise, but on their retirement its founders vested all its shares in a private foundation. In the early 1980s about a quarter of the shares were sold publicly, with three-quarters remaining with a not-for-profit philanthropic foundation.

By 1990, based on the profits from a series of leading drugs, this foundation became the largest single source of charitable research in the UK. In 1990 it spent over £100 million ($180 million) on medical and

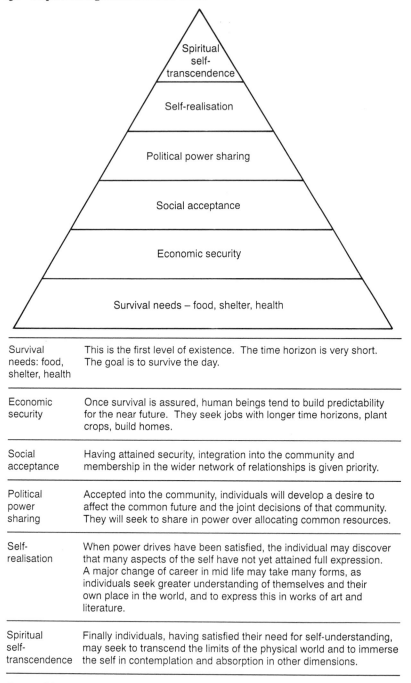

Survival needs: food, shelter, health	This is the first level of existence. The time horizon is very short. The goal is to survive the day.
Economic security	Once survival is assured, human beings tend to build predictability for the near future. They seek jobs with longer time horizons, plant crops, build homes.
Social acceptance	Having attained security, integration into the community and membership in the wider network of relationships is given priority.
Political power sharing	Accepted into the community, individuals will develop a desire to affect the common future and the joint decisions of that community. They will seek to share in power over allocating common resources.
Self-realisation	When power drives have been satisfied, the individual may discover that many aspects of the self have not yet attained full expression. A major change of career in mid life may take many forms, as individuals seek greater understanding of themselves and their own place in the world, and to express this in works of art and literature.
Spiritual self-transcendence	Finally individuals, having satisfied their need for self-understanding, may seek to transcend the limits of the physical world and to immerse the self in contemplation and absorption in other dimensions.

Source: Adapted from Maslow 1954

Figure 9.1 Maslow's needs hierarchy: a brief summary

pharmacological research and on other health-care related activities. Much of the research activity is focused on pure research and on issues of community medicine. These areas enhance the public image of Wellcome and thus help to ensure its continued acceptability as a major supplier of pharmaceuticals to the publicly-owned National Health Service. Much of this activity is fed back into the successful line of drugs, which includes a range of anti-AIDS treatments. The company is thus highly profitable, and its ethical mission complements its conventional market and profit-maintaining activities.

The company's charitable activities enable the management and employees of Wellcome to experience that form of self-realisation which comes from acts of altruism. Their social and political influence is well established, and in the early 1990s Wellcome's corporate environmental programme is well under way. The company is identified with a wider self-interest than that of its employees, shareholders and patients with whom the drugs are successful.

Another, older, example is that of Cadbury. In the mid-nineteenth century, the Cadbury family used their famous chocolate business at Bourneville near Birmingham to found a model industrial community. They pioneered employer-based model housing estates, health care, pensions and unemployment benefits.

Other European companies are evolving environmental missions which reflect the higher stages of Maslow's needs hierarchy, as well as an ethical profile based upon more than next season's bottom line. The German automobile giants Volkswagen and BMW are aiming at the zero-emission vehicle by the turn of the next century. The Japanese, although rooted in a non-western value system, will presumably wish to continue their export success by adapting to western standards: three-quarters of Japan's 1991 trade surplus in the USA arose from car imports. They can thus be expected to offer a generation of environmentally-adapted cars by the turn of the century. Similarly the world stature of Japanese business leaders will benefit.

SUMMARY

A company's environmental performance will increasingly be seen as an important secondary 'product' by its employees and customers. Buyers will see environmental success and public recognition of this success as part of a value-added bonus which increases the overall attractiveness of the business as a partner. For instance, suppliers of cleaning products to supermarket chains are increasingly finding that stores will give enhanced display to their environmentally-updated product lines, since these lines attract higher margins than do other cleaning products.

Particularly in industries with substantial environmental impacts – such as manufacturing, chemical processing, freight distribution – high performance in environmental fields is increasingly seen to assist the company's competitive advantage. For these reasons, many leading chemical-industry companies, like Dow, Dupont and Norsk Hydro, are placing far more resources into environmental programmes than the minimum required under current laws.

The advantages of environmental programmes to a company are in marketing, where environmental performance is seen as part of overall Total Quality Management. Code compliance is an underlying and unavoidable driving force. But codes tend to be succeeded by ever-tighter controls. Solutions that looked workable and viable as environmental standards can rapidly be made obsolete by changing expectations.

Customers also exist inside the organisation in the form of receivers of internal services. The environmental programme can be seen as part of a company's internal relationships. Specific environmental success – through awards and external recognition – can help the company's overall reputation and marketing. High levels of commitment to improvements in its environmental performance stand alongside other quality indicators.

The force of the worldwide environmental debate has moved successively from issues of doubt and substantive analysis into issues of compliance, increasing expectation of improved environmental performance and anticipatory 'proactivity'. Major businesses are increasingly expected to overachieve environmental targets, rather than to respond laggardly to legislation, as indicated in Figure 9.2. The driving forces are insurance and investment markets, as well as consumer preferences.

Notes

1 Professor Prahalad of the University of Michigan and Gary Hamel of the London Business School have developed these concepts.
2 Christoper Lorenz (*Financial Times*, 7 February 1992) on the study *Building Flexible Companies*, published in a private edition by Business International London 1991–2, telefax reference (44) 322–289194.
3 The literature on quality assurance and management is enormous. A recent competent summary is Edgar Wille's (1992) *Quality: Achieving Excellence*.

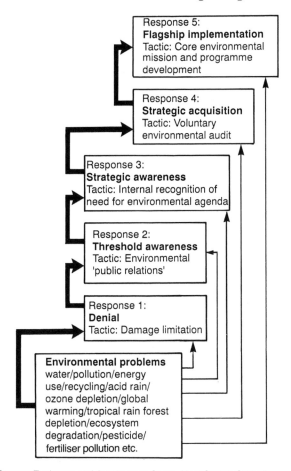

Source: Environmental Assessment Group, Kent County Council;
IMRIC EcoCommunity Programme, University of Greenwich

Figure 9.2 Corporate strategic response and environmental challenges

REFERENCES AND BIBLIOGRAPHY

Adams, R., Carruthers, J. and Hamill, S. (1991) *Changing Corporate Values: A Guide to Social and Environmental Policy and Practice in Britain's Top Companies*, Kogan Page, New Consumer, London.

Allison, L. (1991) *Ecology and Utility: The Philosophical Dilemmas of Planetary Management*, Leicester University Press, London.

Arnold, Davies Cooper (1991) *Clean-up or Close up: Environmental Compliance in Europe*, Environmental Law Report, London.

Arthur D. Little Inc. (1983) *Benefits to Industry of Environmental Auditing*, Centre for Environmental Assurance, Cambridge, Mass., USA.

Association of County Councils, District Councils and Metropolitan Authorities (1990) 'Environmental Practice in Local Government'.

Association of Environmental Consultancies (1991) 'Qualified Environmental Auditors: Code of Practice and Registration'.

Barde, J.P. and Pearce, D.W. (1991) *Valuing the Environment*, Earthscan, London.

Barrett, B. and Therivel, R. (1991) *Environmental Policy and Impact Assessment in Japan*, Routledge, London.

Barrett, B. (1991) 'Japan and the Global Environment: A Case for Leadership', *Japan Digest (UK)*, July 1991, pp. 29–35.

Boseman, G. and Phatak, A. (1989) *Strategic Managment: Text and Cases*, 2nd ed, J. Wiley, New York and Chichester.

British Standards Institution (1991) *Environmental Management Systems*, BSI Sales, Linford Wood, Milton Keynes, MK14 6LE.

Burall, P. (1991) *Green Design*, Design Council, London.

Cahill, L.B., ed. (1987) *Environmental Audits*, Government Press Institute, Rockville, USA.

Cairncross, F. (1991) *Costing the Earth*, The Economist Books, London.

California, State of (1986) *California Environmental Quality Act*, Office of Planning and Research, 1400 Tenth Street, Sacramento, CA 95814, USA.

Carson, R. (1962) *Silent Spring*, Random House, New York.

Chandler, A. (1939) *Strategy and Structure*, Doubleday, New York.

Chartered Association of Certified Accountants (1990) *The Greening of Accountancy: The Profession after Pearce*, ACCA Certified Research Report No. 17, R.H. Gray, London.

Confederation of British Industries (1990) *Narrowing the Gap*, Centre Point, 103 New Oxford Street, London WC1A 1DU.

Cook, S. (1991) 'Environmental Audits: Theory and Practice', *European Environment*, (Brussels) pp. 2–6.

Crawford, M. (1991) 'Green Futures on Wall Street', *New Scientist*, 5 January 1991, pp. 38–9.

Department of the Environment (1989) *Environmental Assessment: A Guide to the Procedures*, HMSO, London.

Economist, The (London) (1991) 'California cashes in on cleaning up', 16 November 1991, pp. 117–20.

EC Committee of the American Chamber of Commerce (1988) 'Industry Experience with Environmental Integration', US Council for International Business Seminars, Brussels, March.

Elkington, J. (1986) *The Green Designer*, Gollancz, London.

Elkington, J. and Hailes, J. (1988) *The Green Consumer Guide*, Gollancz, London.

Elkington, J., Knight, P. and Hailes, J. (1991) *The Green Business Guide*, Gollancz, London.

Environment Business (1990) 'Industrial Environmental Auditing', Supplement, September.

Environment Business (1991) 'Industrial Environmental Auditing Update', Supplement, November.

Environment Council (1990) *The Environmental Audit in Context*, 80 York Way, London N1 9AG.

European Communities, Commission of the (1991a) Draft Proposal for a Council Regulation Establishing a Community Scheme for the Evaluation and Improvement of Environmental Performance in Certain Activities and the Provision of Relevant Information to the Public (Eco-Auditing), Brussels: Doc. No. XI/83/91 – Rev.4.

European Communities, Commission of the (1991b) 'Draft Proposal for Directive on the Environmental Assessment of Policies, Plans and Programmes', XI/194/90–EN–REV.4, Brussels.

European Communities, Commission of the (1991c) 'Directive for Civil Liability for Damage caused by Waste' (Draft).

Executive Enterprises Publications Co. (1988) *The Environmental Audit Handbook*, New York.

Financial Times Reports: Business and the Environment. Weekly 1989–91.
    7.8.91   Kenward, M., 'Catching the Elusive Vapour'.
    7.8.91   Knight, P., 'Reckitt's Cleaners Cut the Mustard'.
   18.9.91   Dunne, N., 'US Call for a GATT Code on Environment'.
   9.10.91   Lapper, R., 'Industry's Last Chance to Catch EC Directives'.
  27.11.91   Simon, B., 'Sharks in the Water'.
    7.2.92   Lorenz, C., 'Building Flexible Companies'.

Friends of the Earth (1990) 'Environmental Audits of Local Authorities: Terms of Reference', 26–8 Underwood St, London N1 7JQ.

Friends of the Earth (1989) 'Environmental Charter for Local Government', 26–8 Underwood St, London N1 7JQ.

Gilbert, M. (1992) 'Inter-Relationship with the new BSI Environmental Management Systems Standard'. Conference Paper Westminster Management Consultants, London, Jan. 1992.

Haigh, N. (1989) *EEC Environmental Policy and Britain*, 2nd ed, Longman, London.

Harrison, L.L. (1988) *Environmental Auditing Handbook – A guide to corporate and environmental risk management*, McGraw–Hill, New York.

Harwood, J. (1991) 'Issues in Environmental Auditing: Oxfordshire County Council's Environmental Audit', Chapter 4 in Thompson and Therivel (1991).

Hofer, C.W. and Schendel, D. (1978) *Strategy Formulation: Analytical Concepts*, West Publishing, Minneapolis.

International Chamber of Commerce (1989) *Environmental Auditing*, ICC, Paris.

International Chamber of Commerce (1988) 'Position Paper on Environmental Auditing', Document No. 210/285 Rev. 2, Paris.

Jarman, R. (1991) 'The National Trust's Environmental Audit', Chapter 5 in Thomson and Therivel (1991).

Ladd Greene, J. et al. (1988) *Environmental Auditing – Fundamentals and Techniques*, Centre for Environmental Assurance, Arthur D Little Inc., Cambridge, Mass., USA.

Lee, T. et al. (1991) *Policy Implications of Greenhouse Warming*, Report of the Mitigation Panel of National Academy of Sciences, National Academy Press, Washington, DC.

Leopold, L., Clarke, F.E. Hanshaw, B.G. Balsley, J.R., (1971) *A Procedure for Evaluating Environmental Impacts*, US Geological Survey, Washington, DC.

Lovelock, J. (1979) *Gaia: A New Look at Life on Earth*, Oxford University Press, Oxford.

Lynch, D. and Kordis, P. (1988) *Strategy of the Dolphin: Scoring a Win in a Chaotic World*, Laurence King, London.

MacKenzie, D. (1991) *Green Design: Design for the Environment*, Laurence King, London.

Maruyama, T. (1991) 'New Technologies to Protect the Global Environment', *Business Japan*, January, pp. 32–3.

Maslow, A. (1954) *Motivation and Personality*, Harper Brothers, New York.

Montgomery, T. (1991) 'Achieving Quality in Environmental Auditing', Chapter 6 in Thompson and Therivel (1991).

Naisbitt, J. and Aburdene, P. (1990) *Megatrends* 2000, Sigwick and Jackson/Pan, London.

Netherlands, Government of The (1990) *National Environment Policy Plan: To Choose or to Lose*, Ministry of Housing, Physical Planning and Environment, PO Box 20951, 2500 EZ The Hague, The Netherlands.

Nicholson, J.P. et al. (June 1991) *Environmental Analysis of Government Policy: A Strategy Review*, Government of Canada, Federal Environmental Assessment Review Office, Ottawa.

Norsk Hydro (1991) 'UK Environmental Report', Paragon communications, London.

OECD (1991) *State of the Environment Report*, Paris.

Ohmae, K. (1985) *Triad Power: The Coming Global Economy*, The Free Press, New York.

O'Riordan, T. (1976) *Environmentalism*, Pion, London.

O'Riordan, T. and Weale, A. (1990) *Greening the Machinery of Government: A Framework for Governmental Administration in the* 1990s *and Beyond*, Friends of the Earth, London.

Owen, R. and Mundy, D. (1991) 'Green and pleasant plans', *EuroDirector/The Director* (London), September.

Pearce, D.W. and Nash, C.A. (1981) *The Social Appraisal of Projects: A Text in Cost–Benefit Analysis*, Macmillan.

Pearce, D.W., Markandya, A. and Barbier, E.B. (1989a) *Blueprint for a Green Economy*, Earthscan, London.

Pearce, D.W. and Markandya, A. (1989b) *Environmental Policy Benefits: Monetary*

Valuation, OECD, Paris.

Pettigrew, A., and Whipp, R. (1991) *Managing Change for Corporate Success*, Economic and Social Research Council UK, Blackwell Business, Oxford and Cambridge, Mass., USA.

Porter, M. (1980) *Competitive Strategy*, The Free Press, New York.

Porter, M. (1985) *Competitive Advantage*, The Free Press, New York.

Porter, M. (1990) *Competitive Advantage of Nations*, Macmillan, New York and London.

Ryan, S. and Palmer, R. (1991) 'ICI Pushes Ozone-damaging Goods on to Third World', *Sunday Times*, 22 September 1991.

Sharplin, A.D. (1989) 'Union Carbide of India, Ltd – Case study', in Boseman and Phatak (1989), pp. 759–73.

Sheldon, C. (1991) 'The Development of the British Standard for Environmental Management Systems', *European Environment*.

Smith, A.C. and Yodis, W.A. (1989) *Environmental Auditing Quality Management*, Executive Enterprises Publications Co. Inc., New York.

Smith, C.C. Jr. (1988) 'Corporate Environmental Self-Regulation', Conference sponsored by International Environmental Bureau and World Bank, Washington, DC, June.

Street, E. et al. (1991) *Kent Environmental Assessment Handbook*, Kent County Council, Maidstone.

Sustainability Ltd. (n.d) *The Environmental Audit Survey*, The People's Hall, 91–7 Freston Road, London W11 4BD.

Taylor, C. and Press, A. (1990) *Europe and the Environment: The EC and Environmental Policy*, The Industrial Society, London.

Thompson, S. and Therivel, R., eds (1991) *Environmental Auditing*, Working Paper No. 130, Oxford Polytechnic, Oxford OX3 0BP.

UK Department of the Environment (1991a) 'Environmental Assessment of Government Policy: Discussion Paper', Unpublished document for the ECE Intergovernmental Working Group on EAGP.

UK Department of the Environment (1991b) *Policy Appraisal and the Environment*, HMSO, London.

UNEP 1990 *Environmental Auditing*, Technical Report Series No. 2.

UNEP 1991 *Industry and Environment*, Technical Report Series 11, no. 4.

US Department of Housing and Urban Development (1980) 'Areawide Environmental Assessment Guidebook', Office of Policy Development and Research, 451 7th St SW, Washington, DC 20410.

US Environmental Protection Agency (1988) *Annotated Bibliography on Environmental Auditing*, Office of Policy Planning and Evaluation, 401 M Street SW, Washington DC 20460.

US Environmental Protection Agency (1986) *Environmental Auditing Policy Statement*, Federal Register Vol. 51, No. 131, pp. 25004–10.

US Department of Housing and Urban Development (1980) *Areawide Environmental Assessment Guidebook*, Office of Policy Development and Research, Washington, DC.

Vernon, R. (1971) *Sovereignty at Bay*, Harvard University Press.

Vernon-Worzel, H. and Wortzel, L.H., contributing editors (1991) *Global Strategic Management: The Essentials*, J. Wiley, New York and Chichester.

Weale, A., O'Riordan, T. and Kramme, L. (1991) *Controlling Pollution in the Round:*

Change and Choice in Environmental Regulation in Britain and Germany, Anglo-German Foundation, London.

Wille, E. (1992) *Quality: Achieving Excellence*, Century Business, London.

Wille, E. (1992) 'Rise of the quality revolution', *Sunday Times*, 19 January 1992.

Willborn, W. (1983) 'Compendium of Audit Standards', American Society for Quality Control, Milwaukee, Wisconsin, USA.

World Wide Fund for Nature (1990) 'The Environmental Audit – A Green Filter for Company Policy, Plants, Processes and Products'.

APPENDIX A
Elements of Effective Environmental Auditing Programmes

(Extracts from US Environmental Protection Agency, 1986)

Introduction: Environmental auditing is a systematic, documented, periodic and objective review by a regulated entity of facility operations and practices related to meeting environmental requirements.

Private sector environmental audits of facilities have been conducted for several years and have taken a variety of forms, in part to accommodate unique organisational structures and circumstances. Nevertheless, effective environmental audits appear to have certain discernible elements in common with other kinds of audits. Standards for internal audits have been documented extensively. The elements outlined below draw heavily on two of these documents: 'Compendium of Audit Standards' (1983, Walter Willborn, American Society for Quality Control) and 'Standards for the Professional Practice of Internal Auditing' (1981, The Institute of Internal Auditors Inc.). They also reflect Agency analyses conducted over the last several years.

Performance oriented auditing elements are outlined here to help accomplish several objectives. A general description of features of effective, mature audit programs can help those starting audit programs, especially federal agencies and smaller businesses. These elements also indicate the attributes of auditing EPA generally considers important to ensure program effectiveness. Regulatory agencies may use these elements in negotiating environmental auditing provisions for consent decrees. Finally, these elements can help guide states and localities considering auditing initiatives.

An effective environmental auditing system will likely include the following general elements.

I Explicit top management support for environmental auditing and commitment to follow-up on auditing findings. Management support may be demonstrated by a written policy articulating upper management support for the auditing program, and for compliance with all pertinent requirements, including corporate policies and permit requirements as well as federal, state and local statutes and regulations.

Management support for the auditing program also should be demonstrated by an explicitly written commitment to follow-up on audit findings to correct identified problems and prevent their recurrence.

II An environmental auditing function independent of audited activities. The status or organisational locus of environmental auditors should be sufficient to ensure objective and unobstructed inquiry, observation and testing. Auditor objectivity should not be impaired by personal relationships, financial or other conflicts of interest, interference with free inquiry or judgment, or fear of potential retribution.

III Adequate team staffing and auditor training. Environmental auditors should possess or have ready access to the knowledge, skills and disciplines needed to accomplish audit objectives. Each individual auditor should comply with the company's professional standards of conduct. Auditors, whether full-time or part-time, should maintain their technical and analytical competence through continuing education and training.

IV Explicit audit program objectives, scope, resources and frequency. At a minimum, audit objectives should include assessing compliance with applicable environmental laws and evaluating the adequacy of internal compliance policies, procedures and personnel training programs to ensure compliance.

Audits should be based on a process which provides to auditors: all corporate policies, permits, and federal, state, and local regulations pertinent to the facility; and checklists or protocols addressing specific features that should be evaluated by auditors.

Explicit written audit procedures generally should be used for planning audits, establishing audit scope, examining and evaluating audit findings, communicating audit results, and following-up.

V A process which collects, analyes, interprets and documents information sufficient to achieve audit objectives. Information should be collected before and during an onsite visit regarding environmental compliance,[1] environmental management effectiveness,[2] and other matters[3] relating to audit findings and recommendations.

(a) Sufficient information is factual, adequate and convincing so that a prudent, informed person would be likely to reach the same conclusion as the auditors.

(b) Reliable information is the best attainable through use of appropriate audit techniques.

(c) Relevant information supports audit findings and recommendations and is consistent with the objectives for the audit.

(d) Useful information helps the organisation meet its goals.

The audit process should include a periodic review of the reliability and integrity of the information and the means used to identify, measure, classify and repay it. Audit procedures, including the testing and sampling techniques employed, should be selected in advance, to the extent practical. They may be expanded or altered if circumstances warrant. The process of collecting, analysing, interpreting, and documenting information should provide reasonable assurance that audit objectivity is maintained and audit goals are met.

VI A process which includes specific procedures to promptly prepare candid, clear and appropriate written reports on audit findings, corrective actions, and schedules for implementation. Procedures should be in place to ensure that such information is communicated to managers, including facility and corporate management, who can evaluate the information and ensure correction of identified problems. Procedures also should be in place for determining what internal findings are reportable to state or federal agencies.

VII A process which includes quality assurance procedures to assure the accuracy and thoroughness of environmental audits. Quality assurance may be accomplished through supervision, independent internal reviews, external reviews, or a combination of these approaches.

1 A comprehensive assessment of compliance with federal environmental regulations requires an analysis of facility performance against numerous environmental statutes and implementing regulations. Many local governments' buildings, fire, safety and health codes also have environmental requirements relevant to an audit evaluation.

2 An environmental audit could go well beyond the type of compliance assessment normally conducted during regulatory inspections, for example, by evaluating policies and practices, regardless of whether they are part of the environmental system or the operating and maintenance procedures. Specifically, audits can evaluate the extent to which systems or procedures:

1 develop organisational environmental policies which (a) implement regulatory requirements; (b) provide management guidance for environmental hazards not specifically addressed in regulations;

2 train and motivate facility personnel to work in an environmentally acceptable manner and to understand and comply with government regulations and the entity's environmental policy;

3 communicate relevant environmental developments expeditiously to facility and other personnel;

4 communicate effectively with government and the public regarding serious environmental incidents;

5 require third parties working with, or on behalf of, the organisation to follow its environmental procedures;

6 make proficient personnel available at all times to carry out environmental (especially emergency) procedures;

7 incorporate environmental protection into written operating procedures;

8 apply best management practices and operating procedures including 'good housekeeping' techniques;

    9 institute preventive and corrective maintenance systems to minimise actual and potential environmental harm;

    10 utilise best available process and control technologies;

    11 use most effective sampling and monitoring techniques, test methods, recordkeeping systems or reporting protocols (beyond minimum legal requirements);

    12 evaluate the cause(s) behind any serious environmental incidents and establish procedure to avoid recurrence;

    13 exploit source reduction, recycle and reuse potential wherever practical; and

    14 substitute materials or processes to allow use of the least-hazardous substances feasible.

3 Auditors could also assess environmental risks and uncertainties.

APPENDIX B
Key EC Legislation on the Environment Providing Incentives for Environmental Auditing

European Community legislation on environmental issues falls into two parts:

1 Regulation – directly applicable law to all Member States.
2 Directive – binding as to the results to be achieved but leaves Member States the choice of form and method. This is commonly used in environmental matters.

Community environmental legislation can be conveniently divided into six subject headings:

1 water
2 waste
3 air
4 chemicals
5 wildlife and countryside
6 noise.

For the purpose of this book and considering the necessity of undertaking environmental audit to ensure compliance with EC law, the first four categories are the most important. Under each section a brief summary of the essential elements of European law are outlined. This list is by no means fully comprehensive, but it will give managers an indication of the need to conform with European legislation.

The EC is driven to producing legislation that places obligations on the Member States if the desired results are to be achieved. This means that community policy, unlike national policy, is made explicit in terms of legislation which is often very detailed, but which inevitably also leaves some measure of discretion to the Member States. The appendix gives an up-to-date picture of the likely compliance standards which will be imposed on any firm locating in Europe.

This appendix is based on work by Nigel Haigh (1989) and Taylor and Press (1990), and updated material from EC official journals.

1 WATER

The European Community wishes to prevent water pollution at source. The policy involves:

1. Setting minimum standards for water depending on its usage

(a) Bathing Water

76/160/EEC (OJ L31 5.2.76)
proposed 3.2.75 – COM(74)2255

Directive concerning the quality of bathing water.

Binding dates

Notification date	10 December 1975
Formal compliance	10 December 1977
First regular report to be submitted to Commission	10 December 1979
Derogations to be communicated to Commission	10 December 1981
Standards to be met	10 December 1985 (unless derogations given)

(b) Drinking Water

80/778/EEC (OJ L229 30.8.80)
proposed 22.7.75 – COM(75)394

Directive relating to the quality of water intended for human consumption.

Binding dates

Notification date	17 July 1980
Formal compliance	17 July 1982
Standards to be met	17 July 1985 (unless derogations made or dely granted)

Surface Water for Drinking

75/440/EEC(OJ L194 25.7.75)
proposed 15.1.74 – COM(74)11

Directive concerning the quality required of surface water intended for the abstraction of drinking water in the Member States.

Binding dates

Notification date	18 June 1975
Formal compliance	18 June 1977
Standards to be set and met	No set date, therefore presumably by 18 June 1977
Improvements to be achieved	'Over the next 10 years', i.e. by 18 June 1985

Sampling Surface Water for Drinking

79/869/EEC (OJ L271 29.10.79)
proposed 26.7.78 – COM(78)363

Directive concerning the methods of measurements and frequency of sampling and analysis of surface water intended for the abstraction of drinking water in the Member States.

Binding dates
Notification date   11 October 1979
Formal compliance   11 October 1981

(c) Waters that support fish life

Water Standards for Freshwater Fish
79/659/EEC (OJ L222 14.8.78)   Directive on the quality of fresh waters
proposed 26.7.76 – COM(76)401   needing protection or improvement in
                                                            order to support fish life.

Binding dates
Notification date   20 July 1978
Formal compliance   20 July 1980
Designation of waters   20 July 1980
Standards to be met   20 July 1985

Shellfish Waters
79/923/EEC (OJ L281 10.11.79)   Directive on the quality required for
proposed 3.11.76 – COM(76)570   shellfish waters.

Binding dates
Notification date   5 November 1979
Formal compliance   5 November 1981
Designation of waters   5 November 1981
Standards to be met   5 November 1987

Groundwater
80/68/EEC (OJ L20 26.1.80)   Directive on the protection of
proposed 24.1.78 – COM(78)3   groundwater against pollution caused
                                                            by certain dangerous substances.

Binding dates
Notification date   19 December 1979
Formal compliance   19 December 1981
New discharge to be controlled   19 December 1981
Existing discharges to be controlled   19 December 1985

2. Protection of aquatic life from dangerous substances

(a) Detergents
Detergents are covered by five interrelated Directives:
1. 73/404/EEC (OJ L347 17.12.73)   Directive on detergents.
   proposed 16.6.71 – COM(71)655
2. 73/405/EEC (OJ L347 17.12.73)   Directive relating to methods of testing
   proposed 16.6.71 – COM(71)655   the biodegradability of anionic
                                                            surfactants.

3. 82/242/EEC (OJ L109 22.4.82)   Directive relating to methods of testing
    proposed 8.2.80 – COM(80)40   the biodegradability of nonionic
                                         surfactants and amending Directive
                                         73/404/EEC.

4. 82/243/EEC (OJ L109 22.4.82)   Directive amending Directive
    proposed 24.3.81 – COM(81)128   73/405/EEC relating to the methods of
                                         testing the biodegradability of anionic
                                         surfactants.

5. 86/94/EEC (OJ L80 25.3.86)   Directive amending for the second
    proposed 22.5.85 – COM(85)217   time Directive 73/404/EEC on
                                         detergents.

Binding dates (73/404 and 73/405)
Notification date   27 November 1973
Formal compliance   27 May 1975
Exemptions possible   until 31 March 1989

Binding dates (82/242 and 82/243)
Notification date   8 April 1982
Formal compliance   8 October 1983

Binding dates (86/94)
Notification date   11 March 1986

(b) Mercury from chloralkali industry
82/176/EEC (OJ L81 27.3.82)   Directive on limit values and quality
proposed 14.6.79 – COM(79)296   objectives for mercury discharges by
                                         the chloralkali electrolysis industry.

Binding dates
Notification date   25 March 1982
Formal compliance   1 July 1983
Standards to be met   1 July 1983 and 1 July 1986
Commission's comparative assessment   Every five years, i.e. first report was
                                         due 25 March 1987.

Mercury from other sources
84/156/EEC (OJ L74 17.3.84)   Directive on limit values and quality
proposed 15.12.82 – COM(82)838   objectives for mercury by sectors other
                                         than the chloralkali industry.

Binding dates
Notification date   18 March 1984
Formal compliance   12 March 1986
Standards to be met   1 July 1986 and 1 July 1989
Commission's report   12 March 1988 and every four years
                                         thereafter

Cadmium

83/513/EEC (OJ L291 24.10.83) Directive on limit values and quality
proposed 17.2.81. – COM(81)56 objectives for cadmium discharges.

Binding dates
Notification date 28 September 1983
Formal compliance 28 September 1985
Limit values to be met 1 January 1986 and 1 January 1989
Commission's comparative assessment Every five years, but first report four
years after notification, i.e. 26
September 1987.

Lindane

84/491/EEC (OJ L274 17.10.84) Directive on limit values and quality
proposed 7.7.83 – COM(83)422 objectives for discharges of
hexachlorocyclohexane.

Binding dates
Notification date 11 October 1984
Formal compliance 1 April 1986
Standards to be met 1 April 1986 and 1 October 1986
Commission's comparative assessment 11 October 1988, every five years
thereafter.

DDT, carbon tetrachloride and pentachlorophenol

86/280/EEC (OJ L181 4.7.86) Directive on limit values and quality
proposed 28.1.85 – COM(84)772 objectives for discharges of certain
dangerous substances included in List I
of the Annex to Directive 76/464/EEC.

Binding dates
Notification date 16 June 1986
Formal compliance 1 January 1988
Commission's comparative assessment June 1990 and subsequently every five
years.

Titanium dioxide

1. 78/176/EEC (OJ L54 25.2.78) Directive on waste from the titanium
   proposed 14.7.75 – COM(75)339 dioxide industry.
2. 83/29/EEC (OJ L32 3.2.83) (Amendment).
   proposed 8.7.82 – COM(82)430
3. 82/883/EEC (OJ L378 31.12.82) Directive on procedures for the
   proposed 17.12.80 – COM(82)831 surveillance and monitoring of
environments concerned by waste
from the titanium dioxide industry.

4. 89/428/EEC   Prohibits the dumping and discharge
                                             into inland surface waters of waste
                                             from titanium dioxide industry.

Binding dates (78/176)
Notification date   22 February 1978
Formal compliance   22 February 1979
Pollution reduction programmes   1 July 1980
submitted to Commission
Programmes to reduce levels of   1 January 1982
titanium dioxide
Programme targets to be met   1 July 1987
First three-yearly report to be   22 February 1981
submitted to Commission
Formal compliance   31 December 1989
Programmes to be introduced to final   1992
prohibition

2 . WASTE

Waste management policy of the European Community has three main objectives. These are:
- to recycle and re-use waste as much as possible;
- to reduce the quantity of unrecoverable waste;
- to dispose of as safely as possible any unrecoverable waste.

Waste – framework Directive
75/442/EEC (OJ L194 25.7.75)   Directive on waste.
proposed 10.9.74 – COM(74)1297

Binding dates
Notification date   18 July 1975
Formal compliance   18 July 1977
Situation reports   Every three years – first report due 18
                                             July 1980.
This is to assume that the first-year period started with the date for formal compliance – an assumption made by the Commission (see reply to European parliamentary question OJ C178 16/7/80). But the Directive is ambiguous and periods normally run from the date of notification.

Toxic waste
78/319/EEC (OJ L84 31.3.78)   Directive on toxic and dangerous
proposed 22.7.76 – COM(76)385   waste.

Binding dates
Notification date   22 March 1978
Formal compliance   22 March 1980
Situation reports   Every three years – first report due 22
                                     March 1981.

Transfrontier shipment of toxic waste
84/631/EEC (OJ L326 13.12.84)   Directive on the supervision and
proposed 10.1.83 – COM(82)892   control within the European
                                     Community of the transfrontier
                                     shipment of hazardous waste.
85/469/EEC (OJ L272 12.10.85)   Adaptation (Commission Directive)
86/279/EEC (OJ L181 4.7.86)   Amendment (Council Directive)
proposed 3.10.85 – COM(85)511
87/112/EEC (OJ L48 17.2.87)   Adaptation (Commission Directive)

Binding dates
Notification date   6 December 1984 and 17 June 1986
Formal compliance   1 October 1985 and 1 January 1987
Information on permits   31 December 1985
Situation report   1 October 1987, biennially thereafter

Disposal of PCBs
76/403/EEC (OJ L108 26.4.76)   Directive on the disposal of
proposed 10.2.75 – COM(75)38   polychlorinated biphenyls and
                                     polychlorinated terphenyls.

Binding dates
Notification date   9 April 1976
Formal compliance   9 April 1978
Situation reports   Every three years – first report due 18
                                     July 1980.

This is to assume that the report is due on the same date as the report under
Directive 75/442. The Directive is not clear on the point but Article 10 says the
report is to be drawn up within the framework of the 75/442 report (see above)

Waste oils
75/439/EEC (OJ L194 25.7.75)   Directive on the disposal of waste oils.
proposed 20.3.74 – COM(74)334
87/101/EEC (OJ L42 12.2.87)   Amendment.
proposed 24.1.85 – COM(85)757

Binding dates
Notification date   18 June 1975 and 13 January 1987
                                     (87/101)

Formal compliance	18 June 1977 and as amended 1 January 1990
Final date for permits	18 June 1979
Situation reports	Every three years – first report due 18 June 1980 assuming the period runs from the date for compliance (see above).
89/667/EEC	Restricts use of PCB/PCT in waste oils, also benzene, benzidine and salts.
Compliance	21 June 1990

Containers for liquids

85/339/EEC (OJ L176 6.7.85) proposed 23.4.81 – COM(81)187 and 28.10.83 – COM(83)638	Directive on containers of liquids for human consumption.

Binding dates

Notification date	3 July 1985
Formal compliance	3 July 1987
Programmes to be communicated to Commission	1 January 1987
Reports to Commission	Every four years.

Sewage sludge

86/278/EEC (OJ L181 4.7.86) proposed 13.9.82 – COM(82)527 and 25.5.84 – COM(84)240	Directive on the protection of the environment and in particular of the soil, when sewage sludge is used in agriculture.

Binding dates

Notification date	17 June 1986
Formal compliance	17 June 1989
Situation reports	17 June 1991 and subsequently every four years.

3. AIR

'Pollutants in the atmosphere, such as sulphur dioxide, fall back to earth as acid deposits contaminating crops, damaging forests and killing living organisms in lakes and rivers. Airborne pollutants also corrode metal structures and paintwork.

The major causes of this damage to forests, lakes, crops and buildings in the community can be attributed to the combustion of fossil fuels by:

- power plants
- motor vehicles
- central heating plants.

The Commission has estimated that the cost to the Community of this type of atmosphere pollution may be as high as £60 million every year.'

(Catherine Taylor and Alison Press, 1990)

1. Air Quality

Air quality – smoke and sulphur dioxide

80/779/EEC (OJ L229 30.8.80) proposed 25.2.76 – COM(76)48	Directive on air quality limit values and guide values for sulphur dioxide and suspended particulates.

Binding dates

Notification date	17 July 1980
Formal compliance	17 July 1982
Limit values to be met, if possible	1 April 1983
Improvement plans to be submitted to Commission where limit values not met	1 October 1982
Limit values must be met	1 April 1993

Air quality – nitrogen dioxide

85/203/EEC (OJ L87 27.3.85) proposed 7.9.83 – COM(83)498	Directive on air quality standards for nitrogen dioxide.

Binding dates

Notification date	3 March 1985
Formal compliance	1 January 1987
Limits to be met	1 July 1987
Report to Commission	Annually from December 1988

Air quality – lead

82/884/EEC (OJ L378 31.12.82) proposed 16.4.75 – COM(75)166	Directive on a limit value for lead in the air.

Binding dates

Notification date	9 December 1982
Formal compliance	9 December 1984
Report to Commission if limits exceeded	Annually from 1 July 1985*
Commission to publish report	Annually from 9 December 1986*
Commission to be informed of places likely to exceed limits and of improvement plans	9 December 1986*

Limit values should be met   9 December 1987
Plans must ensure limits achieved by   9 December 1989

* There is ambiguity about these dates because although the Directive sometimes refers to the date of notification, which is clear enough, it sometimes refers to the date of 'implementation' which could mean the date of formal compliance (December 1984) or the date by which the limit is to be met (December 1987). Here it is assumed that that date of formal compliance is intended. In Article 3(2) a date of four years after 'notification' is given and in Article 3(3) a date of two years after 'implementation': they turn out to be the same date (December 1986).

2. Emissions

Sulphur content of gas oil

75/716/EEC (OJ L307 27.11.75)   Directive on the approximation of the
proposed 11.2.74 – COM(74)158   laws of the Member States relating to
                                          the sulphur content of certain liquid
                                          fuels.

87/219/EEC (OJ L91 3.4.87)   Amendment.
proposed 16.7.85 – COM(85)377

Binding dates (75/716)
Notification date   25 November 1975
Formal compliance   25 August 1976
Limits to be met   1 October 1976
                                          1 October 1980

Binding dates (87/219)
Notification date   2 April 1987
Formal compliance   31 December 1988
Limits to be met   1 January 1989

Emissions from vehicles

A series of Directives deals with emissions from vehicles under three classes:

Positive ignition engines (i.e. petrol engines)

1. 70/220/EEC (OJ L76 6.4.70)   Directive on the approximation of the
   proposed 1969 – COM(69)939   laws of the Member States relating to
                                          measures to be taken against air
                                          pollution by gas from positive ignition
                                          engines of motor vehicles.
2. 74/290/EEC (OJ L159 15.6.74)   (Amendment – Council Directive)
3. 77/102/EEC (OJ L32 3.2.77)   (Amendment – Commission
                                          Directive)
4. 78/665/EEC (OJ L223 14.8.78)   (Amendment – Commission
                                          Directive)

5. 83/351/EEC (OJ L197 20.7.83)   (Amendment – Council Directive)
    proposed 5.4.82 – COM(82)170

Diesel engines
6. 72/306/EEC (OJ L190 20.8.72)   Directive on the approximation of the
    proposed 1971 – COM(71)1484   laws of the Member States relating to
                                          the measures to be taken against the
                                          emission of pollutants from diesel
                                          engines for use in vehicles.

Diesel engines for tractors
7. 77/537/EEC (OJ L220 29.8.77)   Directive on the approximation of the
    proposed 1975 – COM(75)621   laws of the Member States relating to
                                          the measures to be taken against the
                                          emission of pollutants from diesel
                                          engines for use in wheeled agricultural
                                          or forestry tractors.

Lead in petrol
85/210/EEC (OJ L96 3.4.85)   Directive on the approximation of the
proposed 6.6.84 – COM(84)226   laws of the Member States concerning
                                          the lead content of petrol.

Binding dates
Notification date   26 March 1985
Formal compliance   1 January 1986
Limits to be met   Unleaded petrol by 1 October 1989
This Directive replaced Directive 78/611/EEC (OJ L197 22.7.78) which ceased to
be applicable on 31 December 1985.

Emissions from industrial plants
84/360/EEC (OJ L188 16.7.84)   Directive on combatting of air
proposed 8.4.83 – COM(83)173   pollution from industrial plants.

Binding dates
Notification date   2 July 1984
Formal compliance   30 June 1987

3. Monitoring Air Pollution

Monitoring of forest damage
3528/86 (OJ L326 21.11.86)   Regulation on the protection of the
proposed 14.6.83 – COM(83)375 and   Community's forests against
13.7.84 – COM(84)418   atmospheric pollution.

526/87 (OJ L53 21.2.87)	Commission Regulation laying down rules for implementation of Regulation 3528/86.
1696/87 (OJ L161 22.6.87)	Commission Regulation laying down rules for implementation of Regulation 3528/86.
1697/87 (OJ L161 22.6.87)	Commission Regulation laying down rules for implementation of Regulation 3528/86.

Binding dates

Formal compliance	24 November 1986
Periodic reports	Annually, by 1 November.

Screening for lead

77/312/EEC (OJ L105 28.4.77) proposed 16.4.75 – COM(75)166	Directive on biological screening of the population for lead.

Binding dates

Notification date	31 March 1977
Formal compliance	31 March 1978
Screening to be concluded	31 March 1982

Exchange of information – air

82/459/EEC (OJ L210 19.7.82) proposed 14.7.81 – COM(81)361	Decision establishing a reciprocal exchange of information and data from networks and individual stations measuring air pollution.

Binding dates

Notification date	June 1982
Exchange of information	Annually from various dates from 1 January 1979 to 1 October 1982 according to pollutant for a period up to June 1989.

4. CHEMICALS

The European Community approach has been spurred on by chemical accidents like Seveso (1983) and Bhopal (1984). The emphasis has shifted away from developing legislation specific to particular chemical substances towards an approach to minimise environmental risks associated with all potentially harmful chemicals.

Major accident hazards (the 'Seveso' Directive)

82/501/EEC (OJ L230 5.8.82)	Directive on the major accident
proposed 16.7.79 – COM(79)384	hazards of certain industrial activities.
87/216/EEC (OJ L85 28.3.87)	Amendment.
proposed 5.11.85 – COM(85)572	

Binding dates

Notification date	8 July 1982
Formal compliance	8 January 1984
Initial declarations for existing	8 January 1985
industrial activities	
Annexes I, II, III to be reviewed	8 January 1986
Commission to publish report	8 July 1987
Supplementary declarations for	8 July 1989
existing industrial activities (unless	
waiver granted)	

Chlorofluorocarbons (the ozone layer)

80/372/EEC (OJ L90 3.4.80)	Decision concerning chloro-
proposed 1979 – COM(79)242	fluorocarbons in the environment.
82/795/EEC (OJ L329 25.11.82)	Decision on the consolidation of
proposed 8.10.81 – COM(81)558	precautionary measures concerning
	chlorofluorocarbons in the
	environment.

Binding dates

Notification date – 80/372	31 March 1980
Notification date – 82/795	19 November 1982
30 per cent reduction in aerosol use	31 December 1981
compared with 1976	

Pesticide residues

76/895/EEC (OJ L340 19.12.76)	Directive relating to the fixing of
	maximum levels for pesticide residues
	in and on fruit and vegetables.
80/428/EEC (OJ L102 19.4.80)	(Amendment)
81/36/EEC (OJ L46 19.2.81)	(Amendment
82/528/EEC (OJ L234 9.8.82)	(Amendment)
86/362/EEC (OJ L221 7.8.86)	Directive on the fixing of maximum
proposed 6.3.80	levels for pesticide residues in and on
	cereals.
86/363/EEC (OJ L221 7.8.86)	Directive on the fixing of maximum
proposed 6.3.80	levels for pesticide residues in and on
	foodstuffs of animal origin.

Pesticides: use restrictions and labelling

79/117/EEC (OJ L33 8.2.79)	Directive prohibiting the placing on the market and use of plant protection products containing certain active substances.
83/131/EEC (OJ L91 9.4.83)	(Amendment)
85/298/EEC (OJ L154 13.6.85)	(Amendment)
86/214/EEC (OJ L152 6.6.86)	(Amendment)
86/355/EEC (OJ L212 2.8.86)	(Amendment)
87/181/EEC (OJ L71 14.3.87)	(Amendment)
78/631/EEC (OJ L206 29.7.78)	Directive on the approximation of the laws of the Member States relating to the classification, packaging and labelling of dangerous preparations (pesticides).
81/187/EEC (OJ L88 2.4.81)	(Amendment)
84/291/EEC (OJ L144 30.5.84)	(Amendment)

Paints and solvents

80/781/EEC (OJ L229 30.8.80)	Directive amending Directive 73/173 (OJ L189 11.7.73) on the approximation of the laws, regulations and administrative provisions relating to the classification, packaging and labelling of dangerous preparations (solvents).
83/265/EEC (OJ L147 6.6.83)	Directive amending Directive 77/728 (OJ L303 28.11.77) on the approximation of the laws, regulations and administrative provisions relating to the classification, packaging and labelling of paints, varnishes, printing inks, adhesives and similar products.
86/508/EEC (OJ L295 18.10.86)	Commission Directive amending the labelling requirements for lead in paint.

Binding dates (80/781)

Notification date	24 July 1980
Formal compliance	24 July 1981

Binding dates (83/265)

Notification date	19 May 1983 (lead amendment October 1986)

Formal compliance

19 May 1984 (lead amendment,
1 September 1987)

Asbestos
87/217/EEC (OJ L85 28.3.87)
proposed 29.11.85 – COM(85)632

Directive on the prevention and
reduction of environmental pollution
by asbestos.

Binding dates
Notification date

March 1987

Formal compliance

31 December 1988

Standards to be met for plants built or
authorised before 31.12.88

30 June 1991

Commission to report on monitoring
methods

March 1992

Restrictions on marketing and use of chemicals
76/769/EEC (OJ L262 27.9.76)
proposed 25.7.74 – COM(74)1189 and
29.4.75 – COM(75)186

Directive relating to restrictions on the
marketing and use of certain
dangerous substances and
preparations (initially PCBs, PCTs and
monomer vinyl chloride).

79/663/EEC (OJ L197 3.8.79)
proposed 2.3.79 – COM(79)84 and
19.3.79 – COM(79)123

(First amendment)
(Ornamental objects etc.)

82/806/EEC (OJ L339 1.12.82)

(Second amendment)

proposed 10.10.80 – COM(80)570

(Benzene in toys)

82/828/EEC (OJ L350 10.12.82)

(Third amendment)

proposed 11.1.80 – COM(79)792

(PCTs)

83/264/EEC (OJ L147 6.6.83)

(Fourth amendment)

proposed 1981 – COM(81)573

(Fire retardants and novelties)

83/478/EEC (OJ L263 24.9.83)

(Fifth amendment)

proposed 7.3.80 – COM(79)419

(Asbestos)

85/467/EEC (OJ L269 11.10.85)

(Sixth amendment)

proposed 12.9.84 – COM(84)513 and
17.6.85 – COM(85)302

(PCBs and PCTs)

85/610/EEC (OJ L375 31.12.85)
proposed 7.3.80 – COM(79)419 and
10.9.82 – COM(82)498

(Seventh amendment)
(Asbestos)

Binding dates
Formal compliance 76/769   3 February 1978
Formal compliance 79/663   26 July 1980
Formal compliance 82/806   25 November 1983
Formal compliance 82/828   10 December 1982 (where appropriate)

Formal compliance 83/264   19 November 1984
Formal compliance 83/478   21 March 1986
Formal compliance 85/467   30 June 1986
Formal compliance 85/610   31 December 1987

Worker protection:

Framework Directive
80/1107/EEC (OJ L327 3.12.80) — Directive on the protection of workers from the risks related to exposure to chemical, physical and biological agents at work.

Lead – first daughter Directive
82/605/EEC (OJ L247 23.8.82)
proposed 10.12.79 – COM(79)699 — Directive on the protection of workers from the risks related to exposure to metallic lead and its ionic compounds at work.

Asbestos – second daughter Directive
83/477/EEC (OJ L263 24.9.83)
proposed 26.9.80 – COM(80)518 and
28.10.82 – COM(82)685 — Directive on the protection of workers from the risks related to exposure to asbestos at work.
91/382/EEC — Amends rules

Binding dates
Notification date   – framework   4 December 1980
       – lead   12 August 1982
       – asbestos   21 September 1983
Formal compliance – framework   4 December 1983
       – lead   1 January 1986
       – asbestos   1 January 1987 (1 January 1990 in the case of asbestos mining) 1 January 1993

Preventing risks by testing (the sixth amendment)

79/831/EEC (OJ L259 15.10.79)	Directive amending for the sixth time
proposed 8.9.76 – COM(76)433	Directive 67/548/EEC on the approximation of the laws, regulations and administrative provisions relating to the classification, packaging and labelling of dangerous substances.

Binding dates

Notification date	19 September 1979
Formal compliance	18 September 1981
All dangerous substances to be appropriately packaged and labelled before marketing	18 September 1983
Principles of good laboratory practice to be in effect	30 June 1988

5. ASSESSMENT INFORMATION

Environmental impact assessment

85/337 (OJ L175 5.7.85)	Directive on the assessment of the
proposed 11.6.80 – COM(80)313	effects of certain public and private projects on the environment.

Binding dates

Notification date	3 July 1985
Formal compliance	3 July 1988
Commission's report on exemptions	Annually from 3 July 1989
Commission's report on application and effectiveness	3 July 1990

Information on state environment (CORINE)

85/338/EEC (OJ L176 6.7.85)	Decision on the adoption of the
proposed 14.10.83 – COM(83)528	Commission work programme concerning an experimental project for gathering, co-ordinating and ensuring the consistency of information on the state of the environment and natural resources in the Community (CORINE).

Binding dates

Start of programme	1 January 1985 for four years.
90/2/EEC amending Annex 1 to Council Decision 77/795/EEC	Establishing a common procedure for the exchange of information on the quality of surface fresh water in the community.

APPENDIX C
The Environmental Audit Repertory

1 Elements in a Leopold Matrix

Part 1:   Project Actions

A.   Modification of regime
    a. Exotic flora or fauna introduction
    b. Biological controls
    c. Modification of habitat
    d. Alteration of ground cover
    e. Alteration of groundwater hydrology
    f. Alteration of drainage
    g. River control and flow modification
    h. Canalization
    i. Irrigation
    j. Weather modification
    k. Burning
    l. Surface or paving
    m. Noise and vibration

B.   Land transformation and construction
    a. Urbanization
    b. Industrial sites and buildings
    c. Airports
    d. Highways and bridges
    e. Roads and trails
    f. Railroads
    g. Cables and lifts
    h. Transmission lines, pipelines, and corridors
    i. Barriers, including fencing
    j. Channel dredging and straightening
    k. Channel revetments
    l. Canals
    m. Dams and impoundments
    n. Piers, seawalls, marinas, and sea terminals
    o. Offshore structures
    p. Recreational structures
    q. Blasting and drilling
    r. Cut and fill
    s. Tunnels and underground structures

C.   Resource extraction
    a. Blasting and drilling
    b. Surface excavation
    c. Subsurface excavation and retorting
    d. Well drilling and fluid removal
    e. Dredging
    f. Clear cutting and other lumbering
    g. Commercial fishing and hunting

D.   Processing
    a. Farming
    b. Ranching and grazing
    c. Feed lots
    d. Dairying

e. Energy generation
f. Mineral processing
g. Metallurgical industry
h. Chemical industry
i. Textile industry
j. Automobile and aircraft
k. Oil refining
l. Food
m. Lumbering
n. Pulp and paper
o. Product storage

E.   Land alteration
a. Erosion control and terracing
b. Mine sealing and waste control
c. Strip-mining rehabilitation
d. Landscaping
e. Harbor dredging
f. Marsh fill and drainage

F.   Resource Renewal
a. Reforestation
b. Wildlife stocking and management
c. Groundwater recharge
d. Fertilization application
e. Waste recycling

G.   Changes in traffic
a. Railway
b. Automobile
c. Trucking
d. Shipping
e. Aircraft
f. River and canal traffic
g. Pleasure boating
h. Trails
i. Cables and lifts
j. Communication
k. Pipeline

H.   Waste emplacement and treatment
a. Ocean dumping
b. Landfill

c. Emplacement of tailings, spoil, and overburden
d. Underground storage
e. Junk disposal
f. Oil well flooding
g. Deep well emplacement
h. Cooling water discharge
i. Municipal waste discharge including spray irrigation
j. Liquid effluent discharge
k. Stabilization and oxidation ponds
l. Septic tanks, commercial and domestic
m. Stack and exhaust emission
n. Spent lubricants

I.   Chemical Treatment
a. Fertilization
b. Chemical deicing of highways, etc.
c. Chemical stabilization of soil
d. Weed control
e. Insect control (pesticides)

J.   Accidents
a. Explosions
b. Spills and leaks
c. Operational failure

Others
a.
b.

Part 2:   Natural and Human Environmental Elements

A.   Physical and chemical characteristics
  1. Earth
    a. Mineral resources
    b. Construction material
    c. Soils
    d. Landform
    e. Force fields and background radiation

f. Unique physical features
2. Water
   a. Surface
   b. Ocean
   c. Underground
   d. Quality
   e. Temperature
   f. Recharge
   g. Snow, ice, and permafrost
3. Atmosphere
   a. Quality (gases, particulates)
   b. Climate (micro, macro)
   c. Temperature
4. Processes
   a. Floods
   b. Erosion
   c. Deposition (sedimentation, precipitation)
   d. Solution
   e. Sorption (ion exchange, complexing)
   f. Compaction and settling
   g. Stability (slides, slumps)
   h. Stress – strain (earthquake)
   i. Air movements

B. Biological conditions
1. Flora
   a. Trees
   b. Shrubs
   c. Grass
   d. Crops
   e. Microflora
   f. Aquatic plants
   g. Endangered species
   h. Barriers
   i. Corridors
2. Fauna
   a. Birds
   b. Land animals including reptiles
   c. Fish and shellfish
   d. Benthic organisms
   e. Insects
   f. Microfauna
   g. Endangered species
   h. Barriers
   i. Corridors

C. Cultural factors
1. Land use
   a. Wilderness and open spaces
   b. Wetlands
   c. Forestry
   d. Grazing
   e. Agriculture
   f. Residential
   g. Commercial
   h. Industrial
   i. Mining and quarrying
2. Recreation
   a. Hunting
   b. Fishing
   c. Boating
   d. Swimming
   e. Camping and hiking
   f. Picnicking
   g. Resorts
3. Aesthetics and human interest
   a. Scenic views and vistas
   b. Wilderness qualities
   c. Open space qualities
   d. Landscape design
   e. Unique physical features
   f. Parks and reserves
   g. Monuments
   h. Rare and unique species or ecosystems
   i. Historical or archaeological sites and objects
   j. Presence of misfits
4. Cultural status
   a. Cultural patterns (life style)
   b. Health and safety
   c. Employment

d. Population density
5. Man-made facilities and
    activities
    a. Structures
    b. Transportation network
        (movement access)
    c. Utility networks
    d. Waste disposal
    e. Barriers
    f. Corridors

D. Ecological relationships, such as:
    a. Salinization of water resources
    b. Eutrophication
    c. Disease – insect vectors
    d. Food chains
    e. Salinization of surficial
        materials
    f. Brush encroachment
    g. Other

Others
    a.
    b.

(*Source*: Leopold et al., 1971)

2 Checklist on matters to be considered for inclusion in an environmental statement (Dept. of the Env., 1989).

This checklist is intended as a guide to the subjects that need to be considered in the course of preparing an environmental statement. It is unlikely that all the items will be relevant to any one project.

The environmental effects of a development during its construction and commissioning phases should be considered separately from the effects arising whilst it is operational. Where the operational life of a development is expected to be limited, the effects of decommissioning or reinstating the land should also be considered separately.

Section 1
Information describing the project
1.1 Purpose and physical characteristics of the project, including details of proposed access and transport arrangmeents, and of numbers to be employed and where they will come from.
1.2 Land use requirements and other physical features of the project:
    a during construction;
    b when operational;
    c after use has ceased (where appropriate).
1.3 Production processes and operational features of the project:
    a type and quantities of raw materials, energy and other resources consumed;
    b residues and emissions by type, quantity, composition and strength including:
        i discharges to water;
        ii emissions to air;
        iii noise;

   iv vibration;

   v light;

   vi heat;

   vii radiation;

   viii deposits/residues to land and soil;

   ix others.

1.4 Main alternative sites and processes considered, where appropriate, and reasons for final choice.

Section 2
Information describing the site and its environment

Physical features

2.1 Population – proximity and numbers.

2.2 Flora and fauna (including both habitats and species) – in particular, protected species and their habitats.

2.3 Soil; agricultural quality, geology and geomorphology.

2.4 Water; aquifers, water courses, shoreline, including the type, quantity, composition and strength of any existing discharges.

2.5 Air; climatic factors, air quality, etc.

2.6 Architectural and historic heritage, archaeological sites and features, and other material assets.

2.7 Landscape and topography.

2.8 Recrational uses.

2.9 Any other relevant environmental features.

The policy framework

2.10 Where applicable, the information considered under this section should include all relevant statutory designations such as national nature reserves, sites of special scientific interest, national parks, areas of outstanding natural beauty, heritage coasts, regional parks, country parks, national forest parks and designated areas, local nature reserves, areas affected by tree preservation orders, water protection zones, nitrate sensitive areas, conservation areas, listed buildings, scheduled ancient monuments, and designated areas of archaeological importance. It should also include references to structure, unitary and local plan policies applying to the site and surrounding area which are relevant to the proposed development.

2.11 Reference should also be made to international designations, e.g. those under the EC 'Wild Birds' Directive, the World Heritage Convention, the UNEP Man and Biosphere Programme and the Ramsar Convention.

Section 3
Assessment of effects

(Including direct and indirect, secondary, cumulative, short, medium and long-term, permanent and temporary, positive and negative effects of the project.)

Effects on human beings, buildings and man-made features

3.1 Change in population arising from the development, and consequential environment effects.

3.2 Visual effects of the development on the surrounding area and landscape.

3.3 Levels and effects of emissions from the development during normal operation.

3.4 Levels and effects of noise from the development.

3.5 Effects of the development on local roads and transport.

3.6 Effects of the development on buildings, the architectural and historic heritage, archaeological features, and other human artefacts, e.g. through pollutants, visual intrusion, vibration.

Effects on flora, fauna and geology

3.7 Loss of, and damage to, habitats and plant and animal species.

3.8 Loss of, and damage to, geological, palaeontological and physiographic features.

3.9 Other ecological consequences.

Effects on land

3.10 Physical effects of the development, e.g. change in local topography, effect of earth-moving on stability, soil erosion, etc.

3.11 Effects of chemical emissions and deposits on soil of site and surrounding land.

3.12 Land use/resource effects:
   a quality and quantity of agricultural land to be taken;
   b sterilisation of mineral resources;
   c other alternative uses of the site, including the 'do nothing' option;
   d effect on surrounding land uses including agriculture;
   e waste disposal.

Effects on water

3.13 Effects of development on drainage pattern in the area.

3.14 Changes to other hydrographic characteristics, e.g. ground water level, water courses; flow of underground water.

3.15 Effects on coastal or estuarine hydrology.

3.16 Effects of pollutants, waste, etc., on water quality.

Effects on air and climate

3.17 Level and concentration of chemical emissions and their environmental effects.

3.18 Particulate matter.

3.19 Offensive odours.

3.20 Any other climatic effects.

Other indirect and secondary effects assoociated with the project

3.21 Effects from traffic (road, rail, air, water) related to the development.

3.22 Effects arising from the extraction and consumption of materials, water, energy or other resources by the development.

3.23 Effects of other development associated with the project, e.g. new roads, sewers, housing, power lines, pipelines, telecommunications, etc.

3.24 Effects of association of the development with other existing or proposed development.

3.25 Secondary effects resulting from the interaction of separate direct effects listed above.

Section 4
Mitigating measures

4.1 Where significant adverse effects are identified, a description of the measures to be taken to avoid, reduce or remedy those effects, e.g.:

  a site planning;

  b technical measures, e.g.:

    i process selection;

    ii recycling;

    iii pollution control and treatment;

    iv containment (e.g., bunding of storage vessels).

  c aesthetic and ecological measures, e.g.:

    i mounding;

    ii design, colour, etc.;

    iii landscaping;

    iv tree plantings;

    v measures to preserve particular habitats or create alternative habitats;

    vi recording of archaeological sites;

    vii measures to safeguard historic building or sites.

4.2 Assessment of the likely effectiveness of mitagating measures.

Section 5
Risks of accidents and hazardous development

5.1 Risks of accidents as such are not covered in the Directive on EA or, consequently, in the implementing Regulations. However, when the proposed development involves materials that could be harmful to the environment (including people) in the event of an accident, the environmental statement should include an indication of the preventive measures that will be adopted so that such an occurrence is not likely to have a significant effect. This could, where appropriate, include reference to compliance with the Health and Safety at Work Act 1974 and its relevant statutory provisions such as the Control of Industrial Major Accident Hazards Regulations 1984.

5.2 There are separate arrangements in force relating to the keeping or use of hazardous substances and the Health and Safety Executive provides local planning authorities with expert advice about risk assessment on any planning application involving a hazardous installation.

5.3 Nevertheless, it is desirable that wherever possible the risk of accident and the general environmental effects of developments should be considered together, and developers and planning authorities should bear this in mind.

GLOSSARY OF TECHNICAL AND ORGANISATIONAL TERMS

ameliorative strategy actions aimed at lessening environmental impacts through incremental improvements in environmental performance

CO₂ sinks carbon dioxide traps, such as the open oceans and the rain forests, which provide the major part of carbon dioxide recycling at the global scale

CITES Convention on International Trade in Endangered Species

compensatory strategy actions taken to compensate persons or organisations damaged by environmental impacts

COSHH Control of Substances Hazardous to Health

EC Commission of the European Communities

Economic Commission for Europe a major post-Second World War economic investment agency for the war-damaged economies of continental Europe

ecotoxicology the science of examining toxic impacts of substances on ecological systems

GATT General Agreement on Tariffs and Trade. 'GATT' refers both to the Geneva-based international secretariat and to the series of international treaties signed since the late 1940s

IMF International Monetary Fund. The IMF is the principal international banking regulator, with bases both in Basel and Washington, DC. It issues advisory reports, which member countries often act on, about country credit-worthiness, banking quality and public spending. In line with World Bank developments, there are suggestions that the IMF should conduct environmental audits of its national economic policies, in parallel with financial audits

mitigation strategies actions taken to decrease or remove negative impacts of a particular action

OECD Organisation for Economic Co-operation and Development. The Paris-based organisation of the 24 wealthier members of the United Nations. Primarily a research and conference mechanism

risk assessment a formal procedure in forward planning, used to calculate the likelihood of major accidents. Traditionally it has placed low financial values on highly improbably disasters. Under new legislation, legal action can potentially bankrupt even very large businesses if they bear responsibilities for major disasters. Therefore, risk assessment must now involve contingencies with very low probabilities of occurring but with high potential consequences for business

taxation strategies in environmental terms, the application of either tax relief for compliance, or tax penalties for non-compliance with environmental standards

UNEA United Nations Environmental Agency. Since 1972, this agency has been the major research and information centre for UN activity on the environment

UNEP United Nations Environmental Programme, a research and development programme forming the main area of work for UNEA

UNESCO United Nations Economic and Social Council. Paris-based UN agency, with developing interests in environmental issues

WHO World Health Organisation. Geneva-based research and action centre focusing on health-related policies, including housing, health care systems and environmental health. WHO is showing increasing commitment to environmental management issues

World Bank Based in Washington, DC and dominated by major donors of long-term development funds, including the USA, Japan and Germany. In recent years the World Bank has required environmental assessment of all major capital development programmes it is being asked to support. Environmental audit requirements may also be instituted where continuing loan applications on existing initiatives are tabled

INDEX

Note: Page references to figures are shown in italics.